HEARTFELT STORIES

Heartfelt Stories

1st Edition

First Printing 2017

ISBN: 0-9981893-1-6

ISBN-13: 978-0-9981893-1-4

PROCEEDS FROM THIS BOOK WILL GO TO SUPPORT CARDIOVASCULAR EDUCATION AND CARDIOVASCULAR PATIENT CARE

THE AUTHOR WILL NOT USE ANY OF THE PROCEEDS FOR PERSONAL BENEFIT

HEARTFELT

STORIES

The Life of a Heart Surgeon

OMAR M LATTOUF, MD PHD

Dedication

T his book is dedicated to my wife Lina, who has been a great partner through my many years of training and early career in cardiac surgery, and throughout my professional years as a practicing heart surgeon. She has been the rock of our home, always available for the children and me.

I also dedicate this book to my three children, Rashid, Amal, and Zeena. They have been my three best friends and have encouraged me to document my stories. Along with Lina, they are my best cheerleaders.

My brothers and sisters have supported me and have always been there for me during my many years of study. Their continued encouragement enabled me to attain my goals.

To my late parents, who instilled the love of education, hard work, and service in my siblings and me, I dedicate my book.

And to all those whose stories I've mentioned in this book, I thank you for the role you have played in contributing in a very positive way to my life and I hope you will accept my appreciation and gratitude.

Contents

Acknowledgments

I want to express my gratitude and appreciation to my many friends and colleagues who have encouraged me to write and publish this book.

Professor Michael Johns, MD, Chancellor Emeritus of Emory University, suggested the title "Heartfelt Stories" after I sent him my first draft.

Professor Jag Sheth, Emory's distinguished Professor of Marketing and internationally recognized speaker and author in the field, made valuable edits and suggested I transform the book into a movie.

Mr. Inad Kurdi, my childhood friend and a highly-respected documentary producer, was kind to make important edits and provide excellent suggestions, as did his lovely daughter Kinda, a film producer in her own right.

Ms. Pam Long, my classmate from Hiwassee College from the early 1970's, reviewed and edited the entire book and helped get it "print-ready."

I extend my very special gratitude to Mr. Mathew Levy for providing me with invaluable assistance and support in organizing, producing, and distributing the book.

I also wish to express very special thanks to Mr. Michael Bloomfield, a longtime dear friend, for the important contributions he made in editing the final draft of this book.

Many thanks also go to my daughter Zeena, who insisted that I write this story recollection book.

To all, I extend my deep gratitude for your support and encouragement.

Introduction

L ooking back on my forty-year career as a heart surgeon and providing care to critically ill patients suffering from various illnesses, I have probably operated on ten thousand patients and provided cardiac care to another hundred thousand.

It took me twelve years of elementary, middle, and high school education and another eighteen additional years of college, university, and residency training to become a qualified heart surgeon. I was thirty-six years old before I accepted my first real job as a heart surgeon.

During my long years of training, there were many weeks when my colleagues and I had to work 24 to 36 hours at a time without sleep, caring for patients in the operating rooms or intensive care units. We worked with energy and excitement to provide high quality care and to attain the skills of our chosen profession.

As a young surgeon in training, I had a fabulous opportunity to participate in the early experiences of heart and heart-lung transplantations where I completed over one hundred heart transplant "runs." On these runs, I was flown to different cities across the United States to retrieve hearts from donors and bring them back to be implanted in patients struggling with weak and exhausted hearts. These donated hearts saved many precious lives.

For me, as a young heart surgeon at the time, the excitement of being the one bringing the "life-line organs" to those critically ill patients was unequaled. Flying in a private jet from Atlanta to New York, Houston, or Phoenix to harvest a heart and take it back to Atlanta was super exciting back in the 1980s. The midnight surgeries got my adrenaline rush going each and every time and would wipe away the pain of being without rest or sleep for many hours (or sometimes days and nights).

As I reflect on my career and the endless encounters and many stories, I'm sorry that I can only share a few with you in this book.

I couldn't have selected a better career for myself. If I had to do it all over again, I wouldn't want to do anything else but to be the heart surgeon I have become. I have been blessed by being able to experience many victories in saving my patients' lives. For that, my thanks and endless gratitude go to the efforts of all my nurses, physician assistants, anesthesiologists, cardiologists, fellow physicians, administrators, pharmacists, students, residents, and all my health care colleagues who have participated in the care of my patients.

As I look back, I wish life was all victories, but we all know that it isn't possible. I have encountered my share of defeats. I had to face the failures and had to face death. Every time I lost a patient, I felt a part of me had died, too. Losing a patient continues to be the hardest part of being a physician. And to this day, it remains very difficult to accept.

As you begin to read my book, let me share with you how I became a physician. It began with the slide rule. If you don't know it, the slide rule was the precursor of modern day hand-held calculator. If it weren't for the slide rule, I probably would not be a heart surgeon today!

Back in high school, I always enjoyed math and algebra. These topics came naturally to me. I didn't have to study them, and yet I always had perfect scores. Not so in the languages or arts; these subjects were very much a struggle. The sciences were interesting, even though they required intense work and much attention. But as you'll read in Chapter Four, it was that the slide rule that pushed me out of a career in engineering and into a career in medicine. I have never regretted that decision.

In this book, I will share with you some short stories of personal encounters that have left a lasting impression on my memory and have shaped the person I am today. Many of these are wonderful memories that I still enjoy. While many were hair-raising at the time, I can count them as experiences that have helped shape my life.

I hope you will enjoy them.

CHAPTER ONE

My Christmas Story
Memories and Reflections of a Young Boy

As each Christmas season draws near, my memory goes back to a time when I was a little boy, five-years of age, in KG1 (that's the Middle East term for kindergarten) at Terra Sancta School. Terra Sancta is a Catholic school in my hometown of Amman, Jordan.

I vividly recall, as if it happened yesterday, that the year-end celebration in my class was something to look forward to. I have the most wonderful memories of my teacher, Miss Mary, showing my classmates and me the cartoons of "Jack and Jill went up the hill. Jack fell down and broke his crown...."

As the cartoons ended and we walked out of class heading home for a two-week vacation, "Santa Claus" was standing at the door holding a huge bag full of gifts. Santa would hand each child a bag of candy. Fifty-eight years later, my memory still holds visions of that Santa, dressed in red, handing each child a bag containing sweet and sour, yellow-colored lemon drops. The taste of those lemon drops has never departed from my lips or from my memory.

Christmas was always special in our home. It was a home led by my devout Muslim parents, who prayed five times a day and recited the scriptures daily. On Christmas Day, my dad would take my siblings and me to our Christian neighbors to join in celebrations and to congratulate them on this very special occasion. We would leave their homes with our hands and pockets filled with dates and almond-filled cookies.

My mother, may God bless her soul, was a devout believer. She would seize important occasions to take gifts to our beloved Christian neighbors as expressions of affection and good will. If the occasion happened to be a newborn baby, her gift would always be a golden cross.

Haifa, Palestine, was my mother's birthplace. She told me many stories about Haifa and often spoke about her town, her street, and her neighbors. Many times, she would tell me how she and her Christian and Jewish neighbors living in the same building always celebrated the holidays of all three faiths. Until the day she died, she recounted with affection her remembrances about her former neighbors. She loved them all.

When I visited Haifa for the first time in 1994, I immediately knew the place; simply from the cherished memories of my mother's stories. I found her street, the Christian church, the mosque, and the Bahá'í temple, exactly as she had described. What I saw in real life was the picture she had painted in my mind's eye. My mom left Haifa in 1948, but Haifa never left my mom. She took her memories with her and every time she spoke of Haifa, a happy and yet sad smile appeared on her face.

Since time never stops and I have grown older, even older now than my parents were at that period back then, those sweet memories have refused to age, staying young and fresh. They have remained the memories of a five-year-old child, as if my age was frozen at five years of age. These memories refuse to accept the reality of time and sometimes the cruelty of a real world.

As I travel back to those recollections of my childhood and even now recall memories that still bring joy and happiness to my inner soul, I have come to realize that I had an unfinished job.

> I had never thanked "Santa" for the lemon drops.
> I had never thanked Miss Mary for showing us the Jack and Jill cartoon.
> I had never understood why my mom gifted golden crosses.
> I had never thanked her for her many stories and all she did for our family and others.
> I had never understood why my dad took a five-year-old to celebrate Christmas with neighbors.
> I had never said, "Thank you, Dad, for being a great example of co-existence and showing respect for others."

Now, as a man, I fully understand the meaning of what they did, each in their own way. And now, I must say thanks to each one of you who have shaped me into the person I am today.

> Thank you, Santa!
> Thank you, Miss Mary!
> Thank you, my dear Mom!
> Thank you, my dear Dad!

It took me a lifetime to learn your lessons; but I finally did.

CHAPTER TWO

Chewing Tobacco Is Not for Me!
College and New Friends

T his story takes me back to my late teen years and my days at junior college in the small town of Madisonville, Tennessee, USA. Hiwassee College is a two-year college supported by the Holston Conference of the United Methodist Church. Each fall 800 or so students load up their belongings and make the journey to this little college nestled in the hills of East Tennessee, one of the most beautiful states in the nation. The student body comes mostly from the surrounding small and mid-sized towns. The teachers are super friendly and treat students just like family.

Although I had already been accepted and registered in the School of Mechanical Engineering at the University of Tennessee in Knoxville, I decided to withdraw from UT and register in the smaller community college. Coming from another country to the USA, I felt it was emotionally and academically better for me to start in a small college rather than a big university.

A big university in a large city was very intimidating to me. Now, as I look back, not starting at UT Knoxville was one of my smartest decisions of my life. I am so glad I did exactly that. Had I started at UT Knoxville, I might have had difficulty

5

academically or I could have started off on the wrong foot and derailed my entire career.

Now in retrospect, I've become a firm believer that it's better for one to "ease into" a new environment rather than jumping into the unknown and being burdened with difficult situations that could lead to disrupting future career plans.

Hiwassee College was a great place for a transition life-start. I met many nice people and made friendships that have lasted a lifetime. Forty years later, I still hear from some of my former professors and occasionally see several of my former college friends. We regularly stay in touch by e-mail or on Facebook.

Two of my dear friends were Miss Nancy Yarnell and her boyfriend at the time, Tom Wheeler, both from Clinton, Tennessee. Another classmate of mine was Jack Cox, a noteworthy baseball player for both Hiwassee and the University of Tennessee Volunteers (the "Vols"). These friends were at the core of a wonderful tradition. It became customary on holidays, particularly around Christmas, that Jack, my roommate, Rashid, and I would go visit our friends in Clinton. When my younger brother Azmi joined me at the same college, he started coming with us.

Judge J. D. Yarnell, Nancy's dad, would play card games with "Azmah," as he would call my brother. Mr. Yarnell was the county judge in Anderson County in the Clinton, Tennessee area. He was the epitome of an old, country judge and a fine man.

Now Nancy's mischievous older brother, Richard Yarnell, was always looking for something unique and interesting to do. One Christmas afternoon, he invited Jack, Rashid, Azmi, and me to go over to their farm to shoot guns, walk by the creek, and check on his cows. As we started walking, he showed us his supply of moonshine and offered us a taste. Rashid tried some, but I politely declined.

We continued walking along the creek and chatted some more when Richard pulled a tin out of his blue jeans pocket. He offered me a piece of a brown wad that had a chocolaty look and a sweet smell. He tore off a piece and put it in his mouth, seemingly enjoying the taste.

He offered some to me again. I couldn't politely turn him down twice in a row, so I took a small piece and put it in my mouth and started to chew it. Initially, the taste wasn't too bad, but I made the grave and painful mistake of swallowing some of the brown-colored juice. It was like an explosion had gone off in my head and travelled down to my stomach.

In a flash, I was on the ground, puking my guts out. I've never, ever experienced anything as nasty tasting as that chewing tobacco. I was coughing, spitting, and heaving for the next half hour. It felt like a lifetime of misery passed in those few minutes.

That was my introduction to Tennessee's chewing tobacco. Tried it once, but never again. As we drove home that evening, Rashid looked over at me grinning and said, "maybe you should have tried the moonshine instead." To this day, I still wonder if I should have!

CHAPTER THREE

At This University, You Go First, Sir!
The Dean Said

G etting admitted to an American medical school is the biggest challenge facing every student interested in becoming a doctor. The number of competing applicants is enormous. The pre-medical course requirements are incredibly difficult. The students applying are extremely competitive and only those who can withstand years of difficult, endless, and determined work to make the grades become qualified to apply to a medical school.

Then come the medical school admissions tests, which were difficult and challenging, requiring much preparation. I am sure these tests are just as difficult today, if not more so.

When I decided to drop out of engineering (a story you'll read in a few pages) and switch to pre-medicine, I didn't realize that medical school admission was almost exclusively for students with US citizenships. In engineering school, acceptance was open to international students. Since I wasn't a US citizen, I then faced another barrier to medical school admission.

By the time I fully realized that citizenship was a very important, determining factor in medical school admissions, I had made up my mind that one way or the other I was going to become a doctor!

After my two years at my small and lovely junior college in a small town in the rolling hills of East Tennessee, I transferred to the University of Tennessee (UT) in Knoxville, Tennessee. Here in this intimidating campus I came to continue my pre-medical major in microbiology in preparation to apply to medical school.

Going from Hiwassee College, a school of less than thousand students, to a university of more than thirty thousand presented a vast culture shock. UT was huge. At Hiwassee, I had lived on campus and walked from my dormitory to all classes. At UT, I lived off campus and had to drive to campus each day. To get from one class to another, I often had to take a bus. The university had a celebrated athletic department, too. On some weekends during the football or basketball season, the entire campus and the streets surrounding Neyland Stadium or Thompson-Bowling Arena (then Stokely Athletic Center) would become a sea of orange with fans dressed in orange-colored hats, jackets, pants, shirts, and dresses.

At UT and in Knoxville, sports were like a religion. It seemed that everyone adored sports and lived for college sporting events from one weekend to the next. It was great fun for a while, but I quickly realized it wasn't for me. I knew that for me to succeed, I had to immerse myself in the academic environment. I didn't enjoy the diversion of sports from my education. I realized then that I was one-track-minded and have never regretted it.

In my first month at UT, I decided that I needed to be in a smaller, more academically focused university that suited my specific interests and long-term ambitions in becoming a doctor.

I recalled the conversation I had at breakfast a year earlier in the home of my friend, David Davis. His mom Reba told me about Emory University, a school known for making good doctors. It aroused enough of my interest that I applied there immediately.

I called the Emory admissions office, made an appointment with the director of admissions, and drove down from Knoxville to Atlanta, Georgia. I figured my best chance to be accepted would be if I showed personal interest and met with the people responsible for student admissions. I had heard that your best chances to get anything done were if you showed up in person. So that's exactly what I did.

Also, I believed I would develop a better understanding about what they were looking for in a student and possibly leave a favorable impression with them.

My first trip to Emory was well worth the effort. I fell in love with the small and welcoming campus. The admissions office was amazing and welcoming. The director of admissions took the time to meet with me for nearly half an hour. He explained the admissions process and pretty much let me know that I would be accepted for the winter quarter if I successfully completed my course work for that quarter at UT.

As I was feeling increasingly confident in the conversation with him, I brought up the subject of medical school admissions, since that was the primary reason I was applying to his school. My strategy was to enroll at his college and then find a way to get into medical school there. Emory was, and remains, a private university and as such, a non-US citizen had a better chance of gaining admission than in a state-supported school—or so I thought at the time.

I asked the director of admissions, "Do you give your Emory students who are applying to medical school an advantage over those applying from other schools?" He answered, "It is six of one and half dozen of the other".

I left his office thinking, "six of one and half dozen of the other!" What does he mean by that?

*****

My Emory College experience was well worth the investment in every way. Great universities become great for very special and unique reasons. First, and foremost, because they recognize that their mission is to invest in their students, they direct all their resources toward making the entire institution student-friendly.

After all, a university should exist for one reason and one reason only: to transform students into productive and contributing members of the greater society. The focal point of every college or a university should be the student. Not the buildings, not the football teams, not the basketball teams, not the professors, not the president of the university, but the students. They are the focal points of great universities. The staff and faculty of any university should understand that they are there for one purpose: to make the university a great and welcoming place for students to learn, thrive, be challenged, conduct research, be mentored, and pursue careers, and become the best contributors in the fields they choose for themselves.

During my senior year in college, I started preparing my applications to medical schools. Having very little understanding of the process and how to maximize my chances, I thought I had better seek the opinion of the Dean of Academic Affairs at Emory College. So, I called his office, made an appointment with his secretary, and on that date and time went to see him.

I arrived at his secretary's office a few minutes early and with a great deal of anxiety and anticipation, I introduced myself. She invited me to have a seat, then picked up the phone and called the dean to let him know that I had arrived.

Moments later, a nicely dressed gentleman stepped out of his office and walked toward me, extending his hand, and introduced himself as the dean of the college. We both walked toward his office and as we reached his door, with me couple of steps ahead of him, I paused, and said, "After you, sir." He stared at me and with a cool look in his eyes said, "At this university, I go after you, sir."

We went in. We spoke and he listened to everything I had to say. He gave me all the time I needed; he advised me. And when I finished all my inquiries, he stood up and walked me to his office door, wished me well, shook my hand, and said good-bye.

Having come from a third world country, we were taught that the youngest is supposed to respect the oldest, always. The student is supposed to stand up for the teacher and show him or her respect. We were taught to walk behind the teacher, so this dean created an upheaval in my understanding of the student-teacher relationship.

I went home that day having to rethink the definition of what a university was all about. I started to realize that the university was the home for students to find their future and for the faculty and administrators to be the servers and facilitators to make that happen.

At that moment, a revolution was happening in my soul, as I began to realize that my old concepts about student-teacher relationships had just gotten flipped upside down. In one encounter with the dean of this college, he convinced me that he was there to serve my needs, that I was the future, not him. He taught me a lesson that I have not forgotten to this day. Now, as a faculty member myself, I realize that my job is to serve my students and residents, and not to be served by them, for they are the future of the nation, not me!

I graduated from Emory College and immediately enrolled in the Graduate School of Arts and Science in pursuit of a doctorate degree in anatomy and neurosciences. I became interested in that discipline after taking a course with a medical school professor of clinical neurobiology, Dr. Keith O'Steen. He made this course so fascinating that it made me want to pursue a doctorate in that field as an interim step while applying to medical school.

For the next three years, I took all the basic science classes with the freshman and sophomore medical students, in addition to doing my own pre-clinical research work. Those three years were some of the most exciting and formative years of my life. They inspired my career and helped to formulate my academic and scientific personality for the rest of my life.

The graduate school workload was beyond anything that I had ever tried before. It was simply brutal. Beginning work at 6:00 am and finishing frequently by 2:00 am, I barely got four hours of sleep each night. It was hard work, but it was equally challenging and exciting as I was breaking into a whole new world of science, medicine, and discovery.

Each day I was discovering a new concept, learning a new idea, a new disease, a new diagnosis, and a new phenomenon. It was fascinating and was as if I had left this world and moved into the world of science fiction.

In three years, I completed all the requirements for the Doctor of Philosophy in Anatomy and Neurosciences, passed my qualifying examination, defended my dissertation, and was to be awarded my Ph.D. at the young age of twenty-five years. I was ecstatic.

In order to receive my diploma, I had to get the signatures of all my academic advisors on my dissertation. So, I hand-carried my dissertation from one advisor to the other and they all signed it—except one. He refused to sign it for non-academic reasons, as we had political differences. At the time, I was politically very active in the pro-Palestine movement in the United States. Thus, I had written on the front page of my dissertation a dedication as follows: "I dedicate my dissertation to my nationless people of Palestine." He vehemently objected to my dedication and would not sign my academic document!

Without his signature, I wouldn't graduate. He made a demand of me that I refused to meet. We were in a deadlock and the graduation ceremony was less than a week away. I became extremely frustrated.

It occurred to me to seek the opinion of a fellow Emory student, who has since become a very well respected Washington lawyer. He arranged a meeting for me with the Emory Dean of Students, who listened to my case and in turn, called the dean of the medical School. He asked him to see me.

The next morning, I went with my dissertation in hand to see the medical school dean and explained the issue. He looked at me and said, "Son, go get your cap and gown and show up on Monday at the graduation ceremony."

On Monday morning, I did exactly what the dean had instructed me to do. I went to the auditorium to attend the graduation ceremony and—just as the dean had said—my name was there on the list of the few who were awarded their doctorate degrees.

With degree in hand, I headed home to celebrate with my family. I had achieved a major accomplishment that I had spent three long years working toward.

The dissenting faculty member had signed and a few days later I found out why. I was told that the dean had invited that faculty member to his office, sat him at his conference table and had two documents in front of him; my dissertation document and a letter of resignation. The dean gave the professor the option of signing one of the two documents before leaving his office. He chose to sign my dissertation.

Colleges and universities that put their students' interest first and foremost clearly understand their mission. Those are the institutions of higher learning that will always lead the way to build the future generations of leaders.

Emory is clearly one such University.

CHAPTER FOUR

Great Surgeons Never Die
And the Making of a Heart Surgeon

G rowing up, I always wanted to be an engineer. I loved tinkering with wires, cables, and batteries, and building model planes and cars. Mathematics and the sciences were easy for me. History, geography, and languages were foreign, and I always struggled with those subjects. I'm not sure why, but I always felt at ease solving math problems and learning about chemical reactions and about the speed of things. That included the speed of trains moving from one station to another or the speed of sound or, for that matter, the speed of light. Those abstract concepts always seemed to be easier to comprehend and recall than memorizing and reciting a poem or a verse from the scriptures. Memorizing was difficult, understanding biological or physical concepts seemed so much easier.

Like most children, I enjoyed playing and investigating on my own more than studying what the teachers or my parents wanted me to learn. It was not until I had to face my first challenge in my Jordanian middle school that I was challenged and faced with the real threat of failure.

We were required to sit through a government-required examination before passing into the tenth grade. To fail was unimaginable; thus I applied myself to the fullest. My parents were very surprised with this turn of events. They didn't know what had happened as I had transformed from a child who had never studied before to one who applied himself endlessly!

The taste of success was sweet and from then on, I became a serious student. High grades, even in the topics I didn't particularly care for, became the norm. Languages, history, geography, and religion became somewhat enjoyable. Despite my hard work and doing well in all my school subjects, the memories of my particular aversion to the non-math and non-science topics have never left me.

Even today at the age of sixty-four, I occasionally wake up from nightmares dreaming that I was back in school, about to take a final language exam, having forgotten to open the book that entire year. What a frightening feeling it is and it keeps coming back, year after year. This dream happens to me so often that when it comes back now, I say to myself in my sleep, "Oh, don't worry, it's that same dream again. Ignore it and it will go away!!!!"

When I graduated from high school, I came to Knoxville, Tennessee to pursue my college education. It was engineering I wanted to study—until I took a course the first quarter on the slide rule. Today most people don't even know what a slide rule is or what it looks like; let alone how to use one! After passing the first course in slide rule my freshman year in 1971, I started a second course in advanced slide rule in the fall of 1972. Within two weeks, I had decided that I couldn't memorize all the "jerky" movements that I had to remember to do calculations, and I dropped the class. I knew then that "no slide rule" meant no engineering future. All engineering students had to master the slide rule, as it was a rite of passage. I had to switch my major, all because of the slide rule.

My roommate at the time was a pre-med student. I envied him for learning about biological sciences, chemistry, physics, and microbiology, and it was then that I decided to jump into the same academic track. It was a decision that I've never regretted, although it added another fifteen years to me education. Interestingly enough, one year after I dropped out of engineering, prompted by the slide rule, the hand-held calculator came about and in no time, the slide rule became history. It went into oblivion, never to be seen again on college campuses. To this day I wonder, what would my career would have been like if the hand-held calculator had arrived two or three years earlier! Would I ever have become the physician that I am now or would I have become the mechanical engineer that, as a child, I had imagined myself to be?

One fateful spring day during my sophomore year, my college friend David Davis invited me to spend a weekend at his home in Lenoir City, Tennessee. There, he taught me how to water-ski. It was a very special weekend, not only because I learned to water ski, but for even more reasons. When at the breakfast table, his mom, Reba, asked me, "Son, what are you going to become when you grow up?" "A doctor," I said. "What school are you going to apply to?" she asked. "I do not know," I said. "A doctor. Then you should go to this school in Atlanta, named Emory University. They make good doctors there," Reba said. So, I took her advice.

After finishing my time at junior college, I applied to Emory, was accepted, and transferred to Emory College. Coming from Knoxville, Tennessee, to Atlanta, Georgia, was a culture shock, almost as big as the culture shock of coming from Amman, Jordan, to Knoxville. In January 1973, Atlanta was a "big" city with a population of over 1.5 million people.

Emory was much more demanding than what I had been accustomed to in junior college. Competition was intense and course loads were much greater. In order to make my grades and compete with others, it required constant studying. As an undergraduate, I took an elective course in the medical school on human neurobiology and decided to pursue a Ph.D. in that field.

For the next three years, I immersed myself in studying human anatomy, physiology, biochemistry, pharmacology and so on. After three brutal years to get my Doctor of Philosophy in Anatomy and Neurosciences and another equally demanding three more years to get my Doctor of Medicine degree, I finally graduated as a physician. However, I quickly realized that the ten years of graduate education were barely enough for me to do my first workup on my first sick patient.

I spent the next five years in general surgery. It was exceedingly demanding. The number of hours I worked each day were followed by innumerable sleepless nights. Operating without ceasing for what at times seemed like days, with breaks only to grab a quick meal or have a bathroom break. It was exhausting, but it was a rite of passage.

Training in surgery at Grady and Emory-affiliated hospitals was a much sought-after opportunity for every surgical trainee in the country. Thus, I felt privileged to have a chance work at splendid hospitals with world-class faculty and facilities. It was a very rewarding time and the experiences I gained were second to none. General surgeons graduating from Emory were immensely sought after. We were all well trained—we were The Elite.

In my senior year of general surgery training, a family event led me to interrupt my training and travel to my hometown of Amman to see a family member with heart trouble. During that trip, I came to know a young cardiologist who had just returned from completing his fellowship at the prestigious Texas Heart Institute. In those few days I was in Amman, Dr. Dibs would take me with him to make rounds on his heart patients.

Upon returning to Atlanta, I decided that cardiac surgery was going to be my future. The application deadline to the cardiothoracic (CT) surgery program at Emory was about to close so I went to the CT Surgery office, completed the application by hand, and personally delivered it to the chief's secretary.

To fulfill the requirements, I asked the director of my general surgery program, Dr. Richard Amerson, to write my letter of recommendation. In fact, he must have written a "glowing" letter. I say this because on the day CT surgery applications were reviewed, my hand-written application was nowhere to be found. The reviewing committee had only Dr. Amerson's letter of recommendation as proof of my interest in applying to their program. Had it not have been for his letter, I probably wouldn't have been accepted that year, if ever.

The late Richard Amerson, MD, Professor of Surgery, Emory University (Courtesy of Dr. Richard Amerson II)

While the review committee was meeting, I was called by Professor Kamal Mansour, committee member reviewing the applications, who inquired about my application. I explained that I indeed had submitted it and was committed to a career in cardiac surgery. To my surprise, he told me on the phone, "We will accept you based on Dr. Amerson's letter, but you will need to complete another application." I had always known that Dr. Amerson was highly respected and influential. What I didn't know at that time was that his declarations were so decisive.

That phone call from Professor Mansour couldn't have come at a better time. It secured my training position in one of the greatest and most sought-after cardiothoracic surgery training programs in the world. I am forever grateful to Dr. Mansour for his thoughtfulness and to Dr. Amerson for his amazing letter of recommendation.

I became Kamal's student and resident and learned a great deal from him, and eventually became his partner and colleague. During many years of our association, I always enjoyed seeing Kamal and particularly enjoyed his very special "Egyptian-styled" greetings every time we met when he would say: "Izayak ya habibi," which translates as "How are you my beloved friend?"

Everyone who knew Kamal felt like a beloved friend. That was Kamal's style. He loved life and loved people and was loved by all who knew him.

Years later, when Dr. Amerson needed to have a cardiac surgeon on stand-by for a special heart procedure, he requested that I be at his side. It was another great honor that he had bestowed on me. Dr. Amerson was one of the most beloved surgeons Emory had produced. All the residents who trained under him held him in their highest esteem. He was a profound teacher and a warm, wonderful man.

The late Kamal Mansour, MD, Professor of Surgery, Emory University (Photo provided courtesy of Mrs. Cleo Mansour)

To this date, his memory is alive among his former students, residents, and patients.

Emory had a list of world-class surgeons. My former Chairman of Surgery, Dr. W. Dean Warren, is well-known for the Warren-Salam Distal Spleen-Renal Shunt, an operation Drs. Salam and Warren had devised to surgically treat a deadly condition in patients suffering from portal hypertension. This condition causes severe blood congestion in the liver and spleen, causing a backup of blood in vessels in the stomach and esophagus. This further leads to a rupture of small blood vessels, at times causing life-threatening bleeding. Dr. Warren, in addition to being the Chairman of Surgery at Emory University at that time, was the President of the American College of Surgeons, a position highly regarded and respected by all surgeons in the United States and throughout the world.

Dr. Warren was an excellent surgeon and educator, yet had a tremendous sense of humor, especially with the people he liked. I think I was one of the lucky ones. When I worked on his service, I made a point to arrive at the hospital at five o'clock each morning. I made rounds on his patients, wrote my notes and was ready to report to him by 7:00 am. He rewarded me in the operating room by taking the time to teach and instruct me, even though I was only an intern on his service.

One day, I was dictating discharge summaries on the ward when he showed up, un-announced, to perform a procedure on one of his patients. He saw me dictating and in his distinct southern accent called out, "Omaaaar, come and help me do this procedure." I jumped up and exclaimed, "Yes, sir!" He looked at me and with a smile said, "It's only your career that depends on it." Like an attentive soldier, I assisted him, hiding my smile, and realizing that, in a way, he was paying me an off-hand compliment. Or so it seemed to me!

The late W. Dean Warren, former Chairman of Surgery at Emory University and past president of the American College of Surgeons, third on the right in the front row. Seated to his right Professors William McCarty and Garland Perdue, and to his left, Professors Sam Wilkins, Richard Amerson and William Millikan.

Second row from right; Professors Joe Ansley, Asa Yancey, Michael Henderson, Edward Bradley, Paul Golightly, Waldo Powell, Ira Ferguson, Robert Smith, Douglas Murray, Harland Smith and Atef Salam
(Courtesy of Dr. Richard Amerson II)

*****

General surgery training was extremely difficult. It was time consuming with many long hours at work without breaks. On call all night long, every third night, and in-hospital call every third weekend. Then came a three-year cardiothoracic surgery-training program that made the general surgery seem like a "walk in the park."

Cardiac surgery training was much more demanding than anything I had expected, even after completing five grueling years of general surgery. In general surgery, I did thousands of elective and emergency operations; from hernia repair to major orthopedic trauma, to multi-organ damage in motor vehicle accidents. And the list goes on. Despite all of that, cardiac surgery training was a shocker.

When I started my first day as cardiothoracic surgery resident, I realized that I was starting again as an intern in heart and chest surgery. I was treated as a beginner, as I knew very little about operating on the heart. The attending surgeons, the senior residents, the operating room nurses, the ICU, and the floor nurses all treated me and my co-residents as interns who needed to be taught, instructed, and guided.

I even felt like the cleaning ladies and men around the operating rooms looked at the co-residents and me with suspicion and mistrust! I quickly realized that in order to survive, I had to forget having been a "Chief Surgery Resident" only few days earlier and to accept my new role as a "starting resident" again.

My first day on the job, I was guided into the "heart rooms," receiving instructions from everyone and was shown by my senior resident how to open the sternum. Once opened, we harvested an internal mammary artery and placed the patient on cardiopulmonary bypass. From then on, I was assigned to one operating room, preparing patients for surgery, opening chests, harvesting internal mammary arteries and placing patients on cardiopulmonary bypass.

When that was all completed, the attending surgeon would come into the room and perform the key portion of the operation. Then the anesthesiologist and I would "take" the patient off the heart-lung machine and close the breastbone and overlying skin. From there we would take the patient to the intensive care unit. Every effort was made to ensure that patients didn't need to return to the operating room for further exploration for bleeding. "Take back" to the operating room was always associated with "weak" work and thus was to be avoided.

Training in cardiothoracic surgery at Emory was difficult in the 1980s. The "eighty-hour work week," while currently enforced, was not even a consideration then. My contract with the hospital administrator was simple: "work the hours assigned by hospital administration."

My day would start with the alarm clock going off at 5:30 am. After a quick shower and a sandwich, I would drive to the hospital to be there no later than 6:30 am to make rounds on the several dozen patients in the intensive care units and floors. By 7:30 am, the first case was ready to go, requiring me to be in the operating room on stand-by lest the patient's blood pressure dropped or heart stopped during the introduction of anesthesia and have to "crash" on bypass. Thankfully, such was a rare occasion.

On a typical day, I would "scrub-in" on three heart operations. Usually opening the first, bounce to the second, then move to the third case and finish at 7:00 or 8:00 pm. If I were lucky, I would have had a 10-15 minute break between the second and third case to grab a quick, much-needed lunch. The volume of cases during my training was huge. So was the opportunity to see many complex cardiac cases. To see and do as many cases as possible, although very taxing on the surgeon's body, was always what an aspiring young surgeon wanted. The more cases you scrubbed in on, the more likely the attending surgeon would let you do a more significant portion of the operation.

Learning how to do first-time operations was challenging. Learning how to do second-time operations (that is, "re-do" operations) was a completely different experience. On a good day, heart surgery is fraught with disasters if a misstep transpires. This was the dreaded fear, particularly in "opening" the chest of patients who had had prior heart surgeries. To do so was to increase the case complexity by many levels.

Typically, it took minutes to open a first-time chest and place the patient on cardiopulmonary bypass. For "re-dos," it took an hour or more to carefully reopen the breastbone, carve the heart from the overlying bone, identify the aorta and right atrium and place the patient on bypass. After having done thousands of heart operations, many hundreds of which were second or third time re-dos; even today I dread re-do cases. They are time-consuming, hard on the back, take twice as long to perform and are riskier than first-time operations. There is nothing enjoyable about a re-do operation.

My first year of training in cardiac surgery was brutal. Starting work at 6:30 am and finishing evening rounds by 8:30 to 9:00 pm before heading home for dinner, studying if I had any energy left, catching a few hours of rest, and then returning to work. Additionally, we took all-night call every second or third night. The weekend calls were even more painful. The call began Saturday morning at 7:00 am and continued uninterrupted until all operations were completed on Monday night. It wasn't unusual to spend a shift of sixty to sixty-five hours in the hospital, taking care of patients, rounding, operating, and napping in between.

I vividly recall the times when my wife would show up with a grocery bag full of sandwiches, fruit, and desserts that she'd prepared. Thinking back, without my wife, I don't think I could have endured that brutal cardiac surgery training. Her encouragement was essential to my success.

I recall days when I would wake up and start my day fatigued, keeping myself awake with coffee during the day, with the effect of increasing my hand tremor because of the caffeine. Many times we were screamed at by our professors for not keeping steady hands. As such, it was a constant struggle to choose between staying awake with a bit of tremor or falling asleep during long and difficult operations. I chose the tremor.

In my first year as a cardiac surgery fellow, I became interested in heart transplantation, a procedure that was new at the time. I volunteered my services to become the "heart harvester" by learning how to operate on brain-dead donors after families had consented to donate much-needed organs for transplantation. As a young resident, I became the one called whenever there was a prospective heart transplant. I would assemble my team; ride in an ambulance from the hospital on Clifton Road to DeKalb Peachtree Airport, where a Learjet would be waiting to fly my team to a donor hospital in another city.

The adrenalin rush on those nights and days was awesome. For a young resident to have a team under his command, an ambulance, a private jet, then another ambulance ride to a strange hospital in a remote city was tremendous. Quickly, I began enjoying these experiences. For a short time, I was transformed from a resident to an independent surgeon, treated with the respect afforded only to well-established and highly-regarded surgeons.

During this time, I must have harvested a hundred or more hearts from all over the country. I was flown to Miami, Houston, Dallas, Chicago, New York, Nashville, and the list went on; all in private jets.

Two trips were most memorable. One was on the evening of June 6, 1986. when at about 9:00 pm, I received a call to go to New York City for a donor heart. My wife was due to deliver our first child at any time that week. That very day we had gone to our obstetrician who told us that delivery was likely to happen in the next day or two. We called my wife's mom and dad and they came over to stay with us in anticipation of our first child's arrival.

So, as the call for me to go to New York came, I looked at my wife and asked her if I should go or not. My wife said, "I feel fine. Go ahead." So by 11:00 pm, I was at Emory Hospital being picked up by an ambulance and on my way to "my" Learjet and New York City.

We arrived at the hospital two hours later, examined the donor heart after opening the chest and to my surprise, the heart just did not look as vigorous as prior ones that I had harvested. I called the Atlanta-based team and discussed my observations that the right heart appeared larger than normal, contractions were sluggish, the blood pressure was soft, and the central venous pressure (CVP) was high.

Back then we didn't have transesophageal echocardiograms available in operating rooms to fully examine all cardiac chambers and their functions, so I had to rely on my visual examination of the surfaces of the heart along with the blood pressure, heart rate, and central venous pressure. These parameters determined if the heart was good enough and worth harvesting.

Harvesting a weak heart was the most dreaded fear for me and the team. The only thing worse than a weak heart is a type mismatch. My paranoia on those two issues always kept me out of trouble. I always checked and double-checked that the blood types matched and that the heart looked "good."

On examining that heart in the New York hospital, it just didn't look strong enough to me. I feared that removing the heart after infusing it with protective solutions, packaging it in ice-cold preservatives, putting it in sterile packaging, then placing it in an ice-filled cooler and flying it to Atlanta to be implanted in a critically ill patient would be too much of a risk. That heart just didn't look good enough to harvest.

After a discussion with the team in Atlanta, I turned down the heart and flew back home. Harvesting, transporting, and implanting a weak heart was a recipe for absolute disaster. Implanting a bad heart would have meant immediate death for the recipient, a responsibility I didn't want to take.

In my career of harvesting approximately one hundred hearts, I turned down only two. Also, I have never lost any of my heart transplant patients. In this case, I came back to Atlanta empty-handed with mixed feelings, but I felt I had made the right decision. I didn't want to take the chance and bring back a bad heart. So, I returned home at about five in the morning of June 7, 1986.

Soon after returning to Atlanta, my wife told me that she was feeling contractions coming at regular intervals and was sure that the time had come to go to the hospital. We arrived at the maternity ward about 7:00 am, were warmly greeted by the staff, and ushered into a lush delivery suite. As we were waiting for the doctors and nurses to examine my wife, I sat in a recliner chair next to her and fell asleep. To this day, my wife reminds me that I slept through most of her labor, only to be awakened minutes before she delivered our son, Rashid.

I had heard from other parents how exciting it is when one has a newborn child, particularly the first one. No matter how it's described by others, the experience one goes through can't be described in words. As soon as I held my newborn son in my arms, I felt as if I grew several feet taller. Suddenly, my world became much more colorful and I felt as if that child had given me new powers that I had never imagined before. It seemed that my world had taken on a whole new shape and my life had a new purpose.

After seeing that my wife was well and getting some much-needed sleep, my father-in-law and I went to have a late lunch at a nearby restaurant. As we walked out of the hospital on that sunny day, I felt as if I was walking on air. I had feelings I didn't know existed. It was delightful being a new father.

*****

The other interesting harvest was when a young woman was critically ill and extremely unstable. She needed an urgent heart transplant or else we were afraid she wouldn't last another day.

A heart became available in Phoenix, Arizona—much too far for the 3.5-hour total "ischemic time" allowable for a heart transplant. When we added all the land travel time, plus the air travel time and the time to perform the operation, we were well beyond the total safe time to conduct the operation. Even with a fast Learjet, we could not cut the total time to 3.5 hours.

Faced with such a dilemma, the hospital made a call to the United States Air Force Command and requested assistance in transporting the heart in a supersonic military jet. Sure enough, the request was granted. I traveled with my team to Phoenix via our usual private Learjet, harvested the heart, and a helicopter flew us to a military airport nearby. Two Air Force F-15s were on stand-by on the runway with their engines running. The helicopter landed, and my tall assistant Johnny Mack, carried the heart-containing cooler and handed it to the lead F-15 pilot. The plane immediately taxied down the runway, followed by the second F-15 and both disappeared into the night sky. The second F-15 returned to the base after ensuring a safe takeoff of the lead jet.

We flew back to Atlanta in our "slow" Learjet and from there made it to the hospital. By then, the operation was near its successful conclusion. I learned later that the F-15 pilot pushed the engine so hard that by the time he landed, it had to go through major engine maintenance.

And so it was, it took the United States Air Force along with a team of Emory surgeons to save one young woman's life. That was an awesome experience and a great lesson on how a nation can use its resources and energies to save the life of one of its citizens.

One of my dear former mentors was the late Ellis Jones, MD, a world-class surgeon. He was a perfectionist in the operating room. His operations were more like works of art than complex heart surgeries. He demanded neat operating fields, quiet rooms, and attentive residents, nurses, and anesthetists. He was a very quiet man himself and expected everyone else to pay attention to the operation and be equally quiet. His skill at performing coronary artery bypasses was the envy of every resident surgeon and for that matter, every accomplished surgeon. We all wanted to perform coronary artery bypasses with the "Jones finesse!"

To get to scrub with Dr. Jones was considered a privilege. To have him "assist" in a case was a sign that one had finally made it. I scrubbed in on dozens of cases with Professor Jones where I learned his techniques. I memorized his every step and took care of his patients in the most meticulous fashion. Day after day, week after week, and month after month, I worked with Dr. Jones, diligently performing my portion of the operative procedures and waiting to "move-up" to the right side of the table to perform the "surgeon's" part of the operation.

I had almost finished surgeries one day when the phone unexpectedly rang in the room where Dr. Jones was operating and I was assisting. Gena Specter, the head operating room nurse, a petite, vocal, and quick-witted young woman answered the phone. In a loud voice she shouted, "Dr. Lattouf, it is President Carter on the phone and he wants to speak with you. Can you take his call?" I was stunned!

I had no idea what it was all about; absolutely no clue. I had had no prior contacts with President Carter so why would he call me and how would he know that I was in that operating room at that time of the day? I looked at Dr. Jones and he looked at me with a surprised look in his eyes. I didn't know at the time how to react.

Dr. Jones and I stopped operating and I asked permission to take the call. "Sure," he said. I walked to the phone and said "Hello." On the other end was a female voice and not the man's voice that I had expected. It was President Carter's secretary, not the President himself. She was inviting me to have lunch with the President the following week to discuss a book he was about to release. I gladly accepted the invitation.

As I hung up the phone with the "President," I returned to the operating table, only to find that Dr. Jones had moved to the assistant side of the table and gave me the attending surgeon's side. Dr. Jones looked at me and said, "If you're good enough for President Carter, then you're good enough to do my cases." And so it was that President Jimmy Carter contributed to my education in heart surgery.

From then on, I gained Dr. Jones' confidence and started performing more and more of his cases. Ellis Jones was a truly gifted surgeon, a great teacher, and a remarkable educator. He taught so many students, residents, and surgeons and saved thousands of lives. Not a day goes by without my thinking of him as I apply many of his techniques in the operating room. I affectionately tell my residents as I pass on my surgical techniques to them that I learned them from the late Professor Jones.

Great surgeons never die; they just pass their skills on to their colleagues, students, and residents, who in turn pass them on to their colleagues, students, and residents.

That evening, I unexpectedly ran into Mrs. Beth Jones and her lovely daughters at an event. I shared with Mrs. Jones and her daughters that Ellis, "through his teachings had saved another life that day and that he continues to do so every day as we, his former residents, continue to pass his teachings on to our residents." There were smiles and tears.

The late Ellis Jones MD, Professor of Surgery, Emory University (Courtesy of Mrs. Beth Jones)

CHAPTER FIVE

My First Solo Heart Operation
A New Man Left the Room

T he first solo anything is always very exciting. We can all recall when we were children how exciting it was to be able to ride a bike without the training wheels, all alone and without a parent holding us up. Suddenly, we're rolling down the road without falling down. Pilots also go through a lot of training before they are entrusted with an aircraft and allowed to fly solo.

For a young heart surgeon in training, nothing is more exciting than the first solo heart operation. You feel that you have finally arrived as a cardiac surgeon after so many years of studying, being on call, doing endless workups, making rounds and assisting senior surgeons. Then finally, one day you are operating all alone without an attending surgeon in the room observing every step you do.

To be able to conduct a successful heart operation on your own for the first time gives you a great sense of achievement—and a well-deserved one, I must add. The steps that you must execute accurately and without error, number in the hundreds, if not in the thousands. And that's apart from the precise, specialized techniques that must accompany each step; the techniques are required for coordinating the highly complex series of activities.

Performing a successful and flawless cardiac operation is akin to conducting the most complex team activity. During my resident days, we used to say, "cardiac surgery is a team sport as you cannot do it on your own." It takes an entire team of coordinated and well-trained individuals to deliver a successful outcome.

I was in the beginning of my second year of cardiac surgery fellowship training at Crawford Long Hospital in downtown Atlanta, assisting Dr. Robert Guyton on a scheduled cardiac operation, when something memorable occurred. We had just gone on cardiopulmonary bypass, applied the aortic cross-clamp to the ascending aorta and had begun delivering the cardioplegic solution (the solution used to stop the heart from beating and protect it during such period). The procedure was probably going to be either a valve replacement or a coronary artery bypass.

As we proceeded with the operation, we received an urgent call from the catheterization laboratory (the "cath lab") that a patient was having an acute myocardial infarction (a heart attack) due to a total occlusion of his right coronary artery. He was hypotensive and was having EKG changes indicating a sudden heart attack. His blood pressure was dropping fast, so the cardiologist was placing an intra-aortic balloon pump (IABP) and sending him to the operating room for immediate life-saving surgery.

No sooner than the nurse hung up the phone, then another nurse walked into the room and said, "They are rolling the cath lab patient into the operating room next door. What should we do?" Dr. Guyton looked at me and said. "Leave this case and go and take care of that emergency."

I had managed similar situations many times like this in the past. During my first year of cardiac surgical training, my co-residents and I were accustomed to handling daily emergencies coming down from the cath lab at the main campus of Emory University Hospital. In the mid to late 1980s, angioplasty of coronary arteries was on the rise and the technology was still in its infancy.

Cardiologists then didn't have the equipment that they have today to manage complex lesions and to deal with acute vessel occlusion. If a vessel occluded, chances were more likely that they would send the patient to surgery immediately. Thus, with the large volume of surgeries that they were calling for, we were doing at least one cath lab emergency each day. Some were failed angioplasties and some were patients coming in to the hospital with acute MIs that were too complex for percutaneous intervention.

So, I was very well prepared to handle this emergency and knew exactly what to do. I went to the room next door, helped move the patient onto the operating table, and tucked his arms by his side. The anesthesiologist inserted the arterial line to monitor the blood pressure and had started inserting a Swan-Ganz catheter to monitor the cardiac function and adequacy of blood volume in the various heart chambers.

After this, I quickly placed a Foley catheter into the bladder to track urine output during the operation (another measure we use to detect adequacy of blood flow to the rest of the body and to monitor the patient's inner temperature). As the above steps were being completed, the anesthesiologist sedated the patient, placed an endotracheal tube and connected the patient to a ventilator.

The nurses prepped the patient by applying antiseptic solution to the anterior chest, abdomen, groin, and legs, allowing the solution to dry, followed by placing sterile, surgical towels and drapes.

During those short minutes, I ran into the cath lab in my surgical scrubs with my head and face covered, my surgical loupes (magnifying glasses) and headlight on. I did a quick study of the heart cath, identified the problem area in the blocked heart artery, and immediately went back to scrub and complete dressing in my sterile garb.

Adrenaline was coursing through the veins of everyone in the operating room and the tension was so thick that it could be cut with a knife. We were all charged with saving the man's life.

As soon as I took the scalpel and made the skin incision, I asked the anesthesiologist to give 40,000 units of heparin. The skin was open in one strike of the knife; then came the sternal saw and the breastbone was split right down the middle. Now the heart sac covering the heart (the pericardium) was visible. The pericardium is like the skin of a music drum, tight and hard to grasp with a pick-up. When in a hurry, the easiest and safest way is to make a small incision in the pericardium, then grasp the open edge with forceps (a "pick-up") and open the rest with a pair of scissors. This I accomplished.

The heart was right there in my direct view, beating in a sluggish fashion with the right side distended and already showing signs of weakness from the occluded right coronary artery.

I placed two concentric "purse string" sutures on the distal ascending aorta, pushed a knife-tip into the center of my "purse-string" site and inserted an aortic cannula (a tube made of plastic material). The patient was then connected to the heart-lung machine.

Next, I placed another single purse string suture on the right atrial wall and through it inserted a venous drainage cannula in order to drain blood out of the heart and lungs and divert the flow into the heart lung machine. This machine replaces the function of the heart and lungs during surgery.

As I completed inserting the venous cannula, the perfusionist (surgical staff member who sets up and operates the heart-lung machine) remarked that the activated clotting time (ACT) was above baseline and rising, indicating that enough heparin was in the blood that we could go on with the bypass procedure.

In both elective and non-elective procedures, we wouldn't go on bypass unless the ACT was above 400 seconds. At that level of anticoagulation, no clots would form in the circuit. During life-threatening emergencies, we accept going on cardiopulmonary bypass after giving the patient a bolus of heparin in a secure large vein with proven venous return; we also add it to the pump for an additional measure of security.

Once the ACT is above baseline and depending on the level of the emergency, we may go on bypass earlier in critical conditions and keep watching the ACT until it rises to above 400 seconds. The more critical the emergency, the earlier we may go on cardiopulmonary bypass. We usually consider baseline ACT to be around 120 seconds, so once the count is above 120 seconds this would indicate that a minimal level of anticoagulation had been reached. The closer the ACT is to 400 seconds, the safer it would to go on bypass without fear of clot formation in the circuit. Clot formation in the circuit should be a "never-never" event. It is feared, considered to be a fatal event. Thus, the ACT is always monitored very closely.

Returning to our case, once the venous cannula was in place, the perfusionist confirmed that the ACT was above baseline and rising. I glanced over at Dr. Duke, my able anesthesiologist, who said that we could afford to wait a bit more before going on bypass until the ACT was at least 350 seconds.

Anxiously we waited and monitored the blood pressure, heart rate and EKG. With the Intra-aortic balloon pump (IABP) in place and the patient being fully heparinized, the EKG was less alarming than before. The ST elevation in the inferior leads was still there, but not worse, and the blood pressure with the balloon pump assistance was stable. The ST segment of the EKG is the portion of the electrocardiogram that, with any variation, indicates a heart attack happening (or is about to happen.)

"The ACT is 350 seconds and rising," the perfusionist said. I gave the order to go on cardiopulmonary bypass. Immediately the heart emptied out, the lungs were deflated, dark blood was draining out of the right atrium into the heart-lung machine and was being actively returned by the pump as bright red, oxygenated blood into the aorta via the aortic cannula.

At that point, I applied an aortic cross-clamp and gave cardioplegia to arrest the heart, poured iced saline on the heart to cool it down and to help further protect it. At that point, I could breathe a little more comfortably. The right coronary artery (RCA) was still occluded, but the work demand on the heart had been substantially reduced. The heart muscle strain was slowing down substantially, but hadn't stopped completely.

I asked my circulating nurse to inform Dr. Guyton next door that we were on bypass and had arrested the heart. She did and came back saying, "Dr. Guyton said to proceed with the operation and attach a vein graft to the RCA!" Dianne Bailey, senior cardiac PA at the time, was already harvesting a vein from the leg, looked at me and said, "Looks like it's just you and me here. Better do it right!"

I took the vein from Dianne and prepared it by trimming the very proximal end. We reversed the veins before we used them for grafting by placing the proximal part of the cut vein on the distal coronary artery and the distal vein on the proximal aorta in order for the valves in the vein to be in the same direction as the blood flow.

With one assistant helping and Dianne holding the vein, I exposed the RCA, identified a good segment for grafting, took a tiny scalpel, and made a one-millimeter incision in the anterior wall. I then took a pair of micro-scissors and opened the artery forward for 3 more mm and a backward scissors to open it another 2 mm.

With my very finest sutures and microscopic instruments, I sutured the vein to the artery and completed the distal anastomosis. Once completed, I gave a small dose of cardioplegia solution through vein graft to the right heart. I measured the vein to the desired length, trimmed the excess portion, made a punch hole in the ascending aorta and completed the proximal anastomosis by suturing the vein to the aorta.

I removed the clamp, blood began to flow in the coronary arteries, and the heart started to slowly regain its functionality. The ventilator was turned on and soon we were ready to come off bypass. At that point, Dr. Guyton had finished the critical part of his surgery and came into my room. He scrubbed-in, checked my work, and nodded his head in satisfaction as we allowed the patient to come off cardiopulmonary bypass. The case was completed uneventfully and the patient had a good outcome. He was discharged a few days later in good health.

That evening, after my first solo heart operation, I felt like a new man. It was a most amazing experience and was one of those times in my life that I'll never forget.

CHAPTER SIX

My Most Exciting Operation Ever

No Day Off for the Heart Surgeon

O ne afternoon in the spring of 1988, as a chief cardiothoracic surgery resident, I had been invited to attend and participate in an annual meeting held in a beautiful resort in Austin, Texas. Also attending was Denton Cooley, the world-renowned heart surgeon.

I arrived the evening before the meeting after a long day of surgery in Atlanta and checked in very late at night. For once, I had a good night's sleep without pagers going off or phone calls from nursing stations. These calls typically were for pain medicines, return trips to the hospital to take a patient back to the operating room for bleeding, or for an emergency coronary artery bypass.

I woke up fresh, had a healthy breakfast and went to the reception that was hosted by the one and only Dr. Cooley. There were about a hundred of us in attendance, all dressed up in suits and ties. We all seemed happy to be there. After all, we had the day off from our hard days in the operating rooms, were treated like real adults, and hosted in a very lush resort—all paid for by our gracious host.

Certainly, I was happy to be there for many reasons. I was weeks away from graduating from my chief residency year in cardiothoracic surgery, which meant that finally the time had come to get a real job, get paid for it, and start moving up in life. Finally, it was the end of my "student life." It was also a weekend off at a very nice resort, where one could have some much-needed rest and relaxation.

The official morning proceedings started with Dr. Cooley walking into the auditorium to a thunderous applause. He was introduced as one of the world's most distinguished and leading heart surgeons, which we all knew without having to be told. Truly, it was an introduction he didn't need.

We all knew we were in the presence of a living legend and were thrilled with the opportunity to be in the same room with him and to have his full attention. His legacy preceded him and his stories had filled newspapers and magazines around the globe. Denton Cooley had been written up in the New York Times, Newsweek, and Life magazine, as well as countless medical journals. We already knew a great deal about this icon.

Dr. Cooley began his great lecture on a topic that I can still remember today. He began by describing his technique of repairing thoracic aortic aneurysms. He described how he would place his patients on cardio-pulmonary bypass, cool them down to 18 degrees centigrade and shut off the blood flow to the entire body in order to perform a distal aortic anastomosis.

In 1988 that was a huge operation; only few brave souls would dare to do what Dr. Cooley was describing to us. To stop the blood flow to the entire human body, including the head and brain was no small task, particularly when one had to bring the patient and his brain back to life and be fully functional. Not many surgeons were able to do this with great success. Denton Cooley was one of those who could. That was the reason we were all there. He was talking to us as equals and we were listening intently.

He showed us a video of himself performing the operative procedure. The images were very colorful and clear. Unlike real-life operative fields that are often filled with blood and congested with instruments, his seemed like it was a clean field with no blood, few instruments and with the distal aortic tissue clearly displayed. Next to it, the synthetic graft was being adjoined by a running suture with his elegant hands in a rhythmic fashion, making cyclical moves taking one stitch in the native aorta, followed by a stitch in the graft, one following the other.

As we are watching this well-orchestrated move, the anastomosis was completed, the stitches were tied, and the distal anastomosis was done. How long did it take? Eighteen minutes.

A stunning eighteen minutes! He applied the clamp on the graft and re-established flow through the new aorta. The repair looked awesome and with no bleeding from the suture line. I was impressed and so were all the residents in the room. I had to admit that I was a little jealous, too. Would I ever be able to do a distal aortic anastomosis in eighteen minutes under total circulatory arrest?

What an awesome operation we had seen. Saying to myself, "Denton Cooley is a great surgeon and has been doing this for decades." In my mind, I promised myself. "One day I will do this in eighteen minutes."

As I listened attentively to Dr. Cooley's lecture, a speaker came on the intercom interrupting him with a special announcement, "Dr. Lattouf, please come to the reception desk. You have an important phone call." Dr. Cooley abruptly stopped his lecture. I was puzzled and embarrassed. "Who is interrupting Dr. Cooley's presentation asking for me? What's going on here?" I said in my mind.

With great embarrassment, I got up and walked to the back of the room while everyone else and I were wondering what was going on and why I was being called out of this important meeting!

I had no idea what that announcement was all about! Why and by whom would I be called out of the conference for on my day off? What was going on? I made my way to the hotel front desk and introduced myself.

The receptionist said, "There is a party on the line for you." I picked up the phone and took the call. It was the transplant coordinator at Emory Hospital who informed me that I was urgently needed back in Atlanta. There was a unique operation about to begin in a couple of hours and I was needed for a series of operations. Without my presence, none of them could begin.

I said to her, "Wait a minute! What series of operations are you talking about that require my presence?" She said, "A domino transplant." I said, "Domino what?" She said, "OK, I'll explain. We have a donor at Emory Hospital and the family has agreed to donate a heart, lungs, liver, and kidneys. We also have a patient who needs lung transplants who will receive the donated heart-lung block from the deceased first donor.

"We have another patient who needs a heart transplant and will get the donated heart from the heart-lung transplant patient. We also have a patient who needs a liver transplant and two patients who need kidney transplants who will receive one kidney each. In order for these operations to be scheduled and begun, we need all the surgeons to be available and ready to operate.

"All our surgeons are in town and ready to operate except you. We need you back in town as soon as possible as you will do the heart transplant piece. Do you understand? This operation is one of a kind operation; first of its kind in the United States. So, you figure it out and get back to Emory Hospital in the next two hours."

I said, "It's 11:30 am and I'm in Austin Texas, 30 minutes from the airport. I don't know when the next flight is!" She said, "If I were you, I wouldn't be wasting my time talking on the phone. I would be jumping in a taxi and heading to the airport right now. Good-bye."

I ran into my room, grabbed my luggage, and jumped in a cab. I asked the cab driver to take me to the airport as quickly as possible. The cab driver had a sense of humor and asked, "Do you want me to take you by the scenic route or the shorter route?" It wasn't particularly humorous to me right then.

I ran through the hallways of Austin's airport to the Delta gate looking for the Atlanta-bound flight departing at few minutes after 12 noon. By the time I arrived at the gate, the agent had shut the door, closed his books, and the plane was already taxiing out to the runway.

Without even thinking, I looked at the agent and said to him, "This is my flight to Atlanta. You must bring it back as I must get on it right now!" He looked at me with the strangest look on his face, and said, "What?"

I said, "I am Dr. Lattouf. I am a transplant surgeon and I am needed immediately in my Atlanta hospital to do an urgent heart transplant operation on a critically ill patient. My team has called me and requested that I take the first flight out. Please call my plane back." I pulled out my business card and handed it to him.

He picked up his phone and dialed a number. The plane that had pulled out then stopped and returned to the gate. The door to the plane opened and allowed me to board. There was one empty seat in first class, so I took it.

The pilot came out, looked at me and said, "What's this all about? Why did you bring my plane and me back to the gate? Who are you?" I introduced myself and explained the situation.

In 1988, I was thirty-six years old with not a single gray hair and probably looked younger than what a transplant surgeon should have looked in the eyes of that pilot! He said, "You look too young to be a transplant surgeon!" He looked quite young himself, so I paid him a compliment. "You look too young to fly this big plane, my friend," and I smiled.

We landed at Hartsfield International Airport in Atlanta at about 2:30 pm. A helicopter was waiting for me there and immediately flew to a helipad atop Egleston Children's Hospital. From there I traveled via ambulance across the street to Emory Hospital and on to the operating room.

The operating rooms were packed with surgeons and nurses, each coordinating their own tasks. I had two operations planned for me. The first was to open my recipient patient and get him ready to go on cardiopulmonary bypass by connecting him to the arterial and venous sides of the extra-corporal circulation. Second, I had to go next door to the recipient of the heart-lung block (the donor) and take his good heart out to replace a failing heart. Although the recipient of the heart-lung block had a good heart, he was going to give it up, because back in 1988, we were doing heart-lung transplants and not double lung transplants, as we would do today.

My assistant in surgery was Professor Joe Craver. It was a special pleasure for me to perform this particular transplant operation with my very dear friend, mentor, and former professor. Dr. Craver, one of the greatest American surgeons alive, is credited with training hundreds of surgeons.

Ms. Candy Palmer Steele was my excellent perfusionist. She ran the heart-lung machine during the transplant surgery. As I came into the recipient room with the donor heart, I gave the order to go on bypass, applied the cross clamp, cut out the diseased heart, and immediately proceeded to implant the new one.

My technique of heart implantation was straightforward: first, anastomoses the left atria together, then the pulmonary arteries, then the aortas, then take off the cross clamp to allow blood to flow into the new heart and finish by completing the anastomoses of the right atria together. I took the cross clamp off and re-perfused the heart with blood from the recipient patient and within minutes, the donor heart started to beat slowly, gradually gaining strength and increasing its own rate. Candy Steele screamed loudly, "Dr. Lattouf, shortest total ischemic time ever: 28 minutes!"

Shortly afterwards, the patient came off cardio pulmonary bypass, was moved to the intensive care unit, and had an uneventful outcome. He was discharged a few days later. Dr. Craver was a great help and, as it turned out, it was the first time he had participated in a heart transplant operation. But for the master surgeon he was, he was also a remarkable first assistant, consistent with his being the great surgeon I always knew him to be.

CHAPTER SEVEN

My Very First Private Practice Heart Operation

J une 30, 1988, was my last day as a resident in cardiothoracic surgery. My many long years of training in medicine, general surgery, and cardiothoracic surgery were to come to an end at 5:00 pm on that very day.

For the first time in many years, that night I was going home and wasn't going to have any responsibilities for any patients or any attending physician. Nobody was going to call me that night to ask me to come back to the hospital to take a patient back to the operating room for an emergency of one sort or another.

I went home, slept well, and couldn't believe how free I was feeling. Finally, I was done with my schooling—schooling that seemed to have lasted a lifetime. My elementary and high school education required twelve years and my training to become a heart surgeon required another eighteen years. As an adult, I spent fifty percent more time in school and training to become a doctor and a qualified heart surgeon before I could have a job and earn a living.

It took a total of thirty long years of education and training from KG1 to graduating from my cardiothoracic surgery program to become a qualified heart surgeon.

Had I stuck to my original plan of becoming an engineer, I could have completed my professional training after only four years of college and would have saved myself fourteen years of day and night work, being on call, taking one exam after another and being paid barely enough to survive. And I had had to borrow money to pay major expenses, such as buying a car and/or making a down payment on a home.

Time after time, I had wondered if I had made the right economic decision by spending so much time and energy on my education and training. Should I have truncated it and followed my older siblings' career path of engineering and construction? By the time I was about to receive my first paycheck, they each had already secured their respective economic futures, had great jobs, had each built a home, bought a car, and were living their comfortable and stable family lives.

July 1, 1988, was my first day as an attending surgeon and a junior faculty member at Crawford Long Hospital in Atlanta. I was delighted to finally have gained my professional freedom and felt that I was done with taking orders and instructions from my attending faculty. In fact, I became faculty on that day. At mid-morning on that first day, my pager went off and I had a call from Dr. Henry Lieberman, attending cardiologist at Crawford Long Hospital. He said, "Congratulations on your new job. Do you want to operate today?" "Sure," I said.

He said, "I have a patient who has an acute coronary syndrome and I am unable to open his left anterior descending (LAD) artery. He has other badly diseased vessels and needs an emergency bypass."

I drove down to the cath lab and reviewed the cath results with Dr. Lieberman, and indeed found the patient unstable, even more so than we'd anticipated. He was already on a ventilator and requiring inotropic support to keep his blood pressure high enough to support his vital organs. "And by the way, he has received a dose of STK (streptokinase, a "clot buster") in the outlying hospital when he presented there with an acute MI (myocardial infarction, a 'heart attack') a few hours ago," Henry added. He mentioned this as we were rolling the patient into the operating room.

My team and I promptly started the operative procedure, placed the patient on cardiopulmonary bypass, and proceeded to harvest a left internal mammary artery from the left side of the opened chest and a long segment of vein from the patient's leg. I performed the bypasses, weaned the patient off the heart lung machine and gave protamine to reverse the effects of the blood thinner heparin. We knew the patient had received the STK, so we initiated fresh frozen plasma and platelets to pre-empt non-surgical bleeding.

After spending a couple of hours "drying the bleeding" and placing drainage tubes around the heart and near the left lung, I closed the breast bone and the overlying muscle and skin. Finally, we took the patient back to the intensive care unit (ICU).

In the ICU, the volume of bleeding was large, much more than I had anticipated. The patient was bleeding at a higher rate than we considered safe, well over 500 cc per hour. So, I ordered more blood and blood products and transfused them. I also ordered coagulation studies to check whether his body had corrected the effects of the STK he had received. While waiting for these results to come back, I decided to take the patient to the operating room to check for bleeding from any internal surgical sites.

In my mind I was wondering if the bleeding could be coming from either the aortic or atrial cannulation site. Could a metal clip have fallen off a branch of a vein or internal mammary artery, thereby causing the bleeding? In heart surgery, it's good to be a little paranoid. One of my former mentors used to say that if you're not paranoid, then you're not paying enough attention. I believed him and still think he was right.

I took the patient to the operating room, prepped him, draped him, and reopened his wound. I checked all the usual "suspect" places, but all were intact. I could not see a specific "culprit point" that I could cauterize or stitch and stop the bleeding. It looked like non-specific ooze coming from hard to identify places. It looked as if the bleeding was coming from nowhere and from everywhere! I used the cautery on every tiny little bleeding point I could see. I packed the wound with towels and gauze and waited. We gave more blood products and stood there waiting for the bleeding to stop.

Finally, we convinced ourselves that the bleeding had slowed down enough to close the chest again. By then, it was 3:00 am and we were all exhausted from spending an entire day and most of the night in the operating room. We took the patient back to the intensive care unit. And by sunrise, I went home to sleep. That was my first day as staff cardiac surgeon.

I woke up few hours later and called the ICU to check on the patient. My resident told me that the bleeding had slowed down a little, but the patient was requiring more inotropic support to maintain his blood pressure. His CVP (central venous pressure) had risen to 18 and his cardiac index was less than 2. He also added that the patient was requiring more blood factors to correct his coagulopathy and keep his hematocrit (the volume percentage of red blood cells in blood) up.

This wasn't good news. It meant that we needed to immediately go back in again to evacuate blood that had accumulated around the patient's heart. This accumulation was interfering with the heart function and could cause the heart to fail at any moment.

We returned to the operating room, re-opened the wound, removed some clots from around the heart and lungs, cleansed the tubes that had built clots inside them, emptied blood from the chest cavity, and took another close look at each and every surgical site. By that time, the patient had received numerous units of platelets, fresh frozen plasma, cryoprecipitate, and packed red blood cells to replace the lost blood and blood factors. At last, it looked like the bleeding had stopped so I closed the chest for the third time and took the patient to the intensive care unit. By then, we had in fact corrected the coagulopathy and stopped the bleeding, thanks to the many units of blood factors given and countless more hours of OR time.

In the ICU, the patient was requiring Epinephrine, Levophed, and a host of other medications to support his heart function and blood pressure. These medications in turn supported his various bodily functions and were keeping him alive. We then started noticing that his oxygenation was deteriorating. We obtained a chest X-ray (CXR) and sure enough, it showed a total whiteout of both lungs. The patient had developed a reaction to the blood products we had given him; a condition referred to as acute respiratory distress syndrome, or ARDS. This condition is caused by various problems that lead to lung injury after an accumulation of fluids in the lungs, and loss of aerated segments of the lung tissue causes increased leakage of water and fluids into the lung spaces. This all leads to poor oxygen and carbon dioxide exchange. The radiographic images, worsening oxygenation, and the overall poor condition of the patient were frightening.

ARDS alone carries a mortality rate approaching 50%, even before considering someone who just had a major heart attack and complex heart surgery. It was a very difficult situation: poor oxygenation, weak heart function, and recent complex heart surgery in a patient who had received over fifty units of blood products. To get his blood oxygen level to barely acceptable (in the low 60s on his arterial blood gas), I had to place the patient on 100% oxygen via his endotracheal tube and mechanical ventilator. Even that wasn't enough to deliver the needed oxygen to his blood.

Over the next few days, we had to gradually increase the pressure support on the delivered oxygen until we reached a level I had never witnessed before and haven't since. The positive end expiratory pressure (PEEP) was raised to 40 mm Hg to get enough oxygen to meet survival requirements. A normal patient after heart surgery typically has a PEEP of 5 mm Hg. If the oxygenation is borderline, we may increase it to 7 mm Hg and rarely to 10 mm Hg. I don't recall going above 10 mm Hg much at all. But going to 40 mm Hg was a first and a last for me.

As expected, because of the high pressure on the lungs, the patient developed air leaks, a situation called pneumothorax. In this case, the oxygen leaks were outside of the lung tissue, trapped in the chest cavity. Under pressure, oxygen starts leaking into the tissue planes of the skin and muscle. In its worst state, it creates a condition that makes the patients looks like the Michelin Man.

To treat that, without being able to tell exactly where the air leakage was coming from, I inserted chest tubes in both pleural spaces. By then he had 3 tubes that had been placed at the time of surgery, plus 2 more placed now, for a total of 5 chest tubes. I waited a few hours to let the new tubes work to decompress the trapped air, but it didn't happen. The patient remained inflated like a balloon. His chest, abdomen, neck, and face were all swollen with air. Even his eyelids were shut tight because of the air extending into them. I tried another trick for the chest cavity. I placed a "chest tube" not in the chest cavity, but on the outside of the chest under the skin!

To my surprise and the surprise of others, the swelling began going down. Slowly his lungs started to improve, but for the next six weeks he remained on the ventilator. He did require a tracheostomy, an opening in the neck through which a breathing tube is directly inserted.

We solved one problem and then another problem developed. The patient's liver function started showing signs of deterioration. Bilirubin, a liver enzyme, started rising and kept rising until it reached a level of 34; an abnormally high level by any standard. We conducted different blood, CT, and ultrasound tests, but couldn't figure out the exact cause. We finally suspected it was a combination of the multi-blood unit transfusions, an element of liver injury from the various medications he had received, and periods of low blood pressure.

Three weeks into the intensive care management of this patient with one complication after the other, the wife and two daughters felt his condition was hopeless. There were few signs of any spontaneous physical or brain activity despite all the treatments and support.

One night in the beginning of the fourth week, the family asked that the patient be made DNR (Do Not Resuscitate). In other words, if his heart were to stop, we wouldn't restart it or give it electric shocks. Deeply disappointed that I was about to lose my very first patient, I had no alternative but to accept and respect the family's wishes. Under these circumstances, their request was very reasonable and appropriate. Before I went home that evening, I told the family that chances were high that he would not survive the night without the aggressive medical support that he was currently on. The family requested weaning down much of the medication and to let nature take its course. They called their clergy in and started making funeral arrangements for the next day. I went home broken-hearted and with a heavy sense of defeat.

The next morning, I went to the hospital expecting to be told that the patient had expired or was about to. But to the contrary, the caring nurse told me that his blood pressure and other vital signs had remained stable, even after we removed much of his support. I went to the family and shared with them the relatively good news and asked that we give him more time to show improvement. I said, "If he could survive even after removing many of the medications, then let's give him another couple of days and see what happens."

The funeral plans were put off and we waited. To our surprise, the next day he blinked his eyelids, the first sign of any physical activity since his operation. Gradually, he started to open his eyes, move his hands and feet, and show more and more signs of life. After six weeks in the ICU and another month in the hospital, the patient walked out of the hospital alive and fully functional.

My first patient in private practice did not die. It took so much time and work from so many people to keep him alive, but he lived!

Twenty-four years later, I met a man who knew this patient. He gave me his telephone number so I called him and inquired about his health. He spoke very eloquently and was very well composed. He thanked me for the call and the care I had provided him twenty-four years earlier. I invited him to come to see me in the clinic. He declined, thanked me again and said, "I really don't like to drive in the Atlanta traffic."

*****

Postscript

On Father's Day, 2016, I received this unexpected email from the daughter of this patient:

"I hope that this email finds you well. I wanted to send you a message regarding my beloved father. My father passed away on December 8, 2013, while I was holding his hand and telling him how much I loved him. I thank God that I had him with me for another 25 years after his heart attack in 1988. But I miss him every day. He passed away from congestive heart failure – he was in my home for 25 days under hospice care with oxygen tanks – his congestive heart failure had caused fluid in his lungs and ultimately infection in his blood, for which I was giving him antibiotic injections in his IV that went straight to his heart. He was almost 90 years old."

I wrote her back the following day:

"Nice to hear from you. I often think of your dad, your mom, you, and your sister. It has been a long time. I have actually written a chapter in my upcoming book about your dad's story. It's attached for your reading."

She wrote back:

"Thank you for your reply and thank you for sharing that story with me. You have written it so well. I remember every detail, every procedure you performed, and the exact day that it happened. You have recounted it so accurately and heartwarmingly. I would like a copy of your book when it is completed. Please let me know when it's published so I can purchase one.

"After the conversation we had with you in which I was filled with desperation and loss of hope, I ran to the church across from BellSouth near Crawford Long Hospital, went inside, and it was empty. I went to the front of the church and started crying my heart out and praying to God. I told Him how much I loved my father and how much I would be lost without him—telling Him that 26 years was not long enough to have with the world's best father. I needed more time. There was a Bible next to me so I picked it up and opened it randomly. There was a passage that someone had underlined – and to this day, I will never forget what it said:

"He cleaves on to me with love, so I will protect him. I will deliver him because he knows my name."

"God had spoken to me. A sense of calmness came over me and as I returned to the hospital. My mother, my sister, and my aunt were all distraught and nervous, not knowing what they were doing. I kept telling them that my dad would make it. Baba will make it. And they thought that I was crazy. But I knew. God had told me that He would protect him.

"I just wanted to share that with you. Those memories bring tears to my eyes. Dr. Lattouf, I adored my father. God made you a vessel to bring him back to me for another 25 years. I enjoyed those extra years with him. I drew from his strength, knowledge, and wisdom. In his last days, when he was with me and sick, I remember I was crying and I told him that I loved him and didn't want him to die. He said to me that it was time for him to go. And for me to remember two things: first, he would always be with me. Second, to find in my son what I would lose with him when he died. It took a while for me to know what he meant. When he said, 'he will always be with me,' he meant that what he had taught me—his words, his advice, and his love--would last me a lifetime. When he said to find in my son what I found in him he meant that I should try to get from my son the emotional strength that I had gotten from him.

Dr. Lattouf, I will always think of you as the savior of my heart. May God bless you and your family."

CHAPTER EIGHT

At the White House
Seeing History Being Made

M y wife, Lina, phoned me one afternoon in 1993 and said; "The White House just called for you and left this number for you to call back."

I said, "What are you talking about? Is this a joke or what?" She said, "Actually, when the lady from the White House called and introduced herself as President Clinton's protocol officer, I laughed and told her, "Lady are you joking with me? What's this all about?" And she answered, "Ma'am, this *is* the White House and this *is* a call for Dr. Lattouf. Please convey to him this invitation from the President of the United States, the First Lady, the Vice President, and Mrs. Gore to travel to the White House and attend the Peace Signing Agreement on September 13, 1993. Here's the telephone number for him to call. Goodbye."

I took the number from my wife and called the White House. Sure enough, it was answered by the same staff person at the White House who had talked earlier with Lina. She confirmed that the invitation was real, and invited me to attend the signing of the peace agreements between the leaders of Israel and Palestine in the Rose Garden of the White House.

I was asked to provide copies of my driver's license, passport, Social Security card, a photograph, and my date of birth. I called the airlines to make reservations to Washington from Atlanta and was shocked at the price of the tickets. They were expensive—$750 for economy tickets. I tried to get a hotel room and couldn't find one within a hundred miles from the center of the city.

I had to think. How important is this, really? I could watch this on television and save myself the pain of travel and over a thousand dollars. Or I could spend the money and see what it's like to be at the White House with all those world leaders? I decided to call George Salem, a college friend of mine, a highly-respected Washington attorney who was in the political and diplomatic circles of the Capital, the White House, and so on. I called George that evening and was lucky to get him on his home phone. "Hello George. This is Omar from Atlanta. How are you? I received an invitation from the White House today and I wanted to ask your opinion if you thought it was worthwhile to make the trip?" I said.

"Are you nuts?" he said, "I'm the one who suggested your name! It's an opportunity of a lifetime to be invited to the White House. Do you think you will ever get an invitation from the President of the United States of America again? Sure, you should accept this invitation. And by the way, there are no hotel rooms in Washington. You can come and stay with us in our home." I swallowed my pride and said, "Yes, it is indeed a great idea. I will be attending."

I took the flight to Washington DC and what an amazing sight it was. The city was abuzz with activities. Flags of opposing and warring sides were now flying side by side, which lent an air of optimism to the city. People who had been *persona non-grata* a few days earlier were suddenly welcomed celebrities and were sought after by every news outlet for interviews and meetings. It was history in the making and I had the privilege of being there and closely observing it all!

The morning of September 13, 1993, I went to the White House and was stopped by the security detail. I showed them identification, they cross-referenced my documents with theirs, and allowed me in. Once I entered the Rose Garden, I could walk freely among the guests. It was an awesome scene with guests who were people I'd only seen on television.

There were Henry Kissinger, former President Gerald Ford, former President George H. W. Bush, Chairman Yasser Arafat, Prime Minister Yitzhak Rabin, King Hussein, President Hosni Mubarak, President Bill Clinton, Vice President Al Gore, and an additional three thousand more guests. Getting invited to the White House was an awesome experience. Witnessing history as it was happening was amazing, although regrettably, the events that should have happened afterwards never materialized as the parties had hoped.

That said, it was still a great dream and an enormous experience. Hopefully, the dream of peace between two great peoples will become a reality some day in the not-too-distant future. I hope to see it in my lifetime.

CHAPTER NINE

This Baby Will Not Die on My Watch
Pediatric Cardiology is Not My Cup of Tea

M edicine is a challenging profession. The learning process is huge. It takes many years of dedicated, hard work to study, learn, and master so many disciplines like biology, chemistry, physiology, microbiology, pathology, anatomy, pharmacology, and the list goes on and on and on.

Then come the clinical services, which present a whole new set of learning challenges and responsibilities. On these services, you learn how to treat high blood pressure, abnormal blood sugar levels, and other conditions that would fit in the realm of internal medicine. In pediatrics, you learn to treat diseases and illnesses unique to children. And the list of services goes on to pulmonary medicine, orthopedics, cardiology, neurology, and many more. A major difference with pediatric care is that your patients are now very young, from neonates to teenagers.

The learning on clinical services is very different from surgery, because one learns to deal with real people under real circumstances. It's a little like learning how to repair an airplane while flying at 30,000 feet. There's no room for error, as minor errors could mean major disasters. Any miscalculation could be the difference between good health or illness, and life or death.

Surgeons must learn everything physicians must know and more. We must know the science of medicine and add the art and skills of surgery. To be an excellent surgeon, particularly cardiovascular surgeon, one needs to be a good internist and an excellent technical operator. One without the other doesn't work well.

If mistakes are made by young learners and not caught by their seniors, in due time major disasters can happen. If mistakes are major, lives could be lost. In the practice of medicine the risks are high. The thought of making mistakes leading to injuries to patients, or worse, causing loss of life, is frightening, emotionally painful, and extremely stressful to everyone involved. This extends most of all to the patient's loved ones. The mere thought of a medical error weighs heavily on every health care provider and every decision maker in the health care system across the country and around the world.

Errors in medicine vary in their outcomes. Some mild errors may cause no noticeable problems while others may cause severe problems and irreparable damage. Not giving a medication dose, such as a pain medicine, an antibiotic, or a sleep agent can interfere with patient's comfort or clinical progress. Other errors may have life-threatening consequences. If a doctor or a nurse gives a large dose of insulin to a hospitalized patient, it may lead to a severe drop in blood sugar which can cause the patient to lose vital energy supply to the brain and lose consciousness. If not immediately identified and corrected, permanent brain damage or even death may occur.

Pain management is another troubling area in hospitals. Patients have the right to be pain-free after procedures and should receive the right amount and type of analgesic medicine to control pain. However, if a patient gets an overdose of morphine leading to him or her failing to breathe, it can turn into a full blown cardiorespiratory arrest. This medical emergency can lead to very undesirable outcomes, including death. As serious as the worst medical error can be, surgical errors often are even worse and more dramatic. Surgical errors have immediate effects with potentially catastrophic results.

In surgery, unlike in medicine, once you cut an organ, you cannot give an antidote to reverse that cut. Once you remove an organ, it may be impossible to suture it back in place. A repair is much more challenging, time-consuming, costly, and fraught with even higher risks. Surgical errors, particularly in the cardiovascular system, are simply much more dangerous. When they happen, they are explosive in nature, with much blood loss and a rapid loss of vital signs; they are much more difficult to correct. Death can occur in minutes, if not seconds.

When surgical errors occur, the repair or "fix" must be rapid, immediate, accurate, and curative. All this must happen in one swift series of actions. And that isn't easy to do. To accomplish this, a surgeon must have a very special skill set and have been through many similar, complex surgical procedures before. He/she must have rehearsed high-risk situations in advance of their happening or have at least witnessed them.

In my recollection of interesting cases, several stand out; they are hard to forget. I recall one day when I was completing a coronary artery bypass procedure, I was called into another operating room where a patient was undergoing an abdominal procedure. The young surgeon had encountered massive and unexpected bleeding in the abdomen while inserting a laparoscope. As I was guided into the room, the patient's blood pressure was dropping quickly and the bleeding was substantial. I took one look at the monitor and saw the systolic blood pressure at 80. I looked at the abdomen and the entry points of the laparoscope, the direction of applied force and assessed which vessels would be the in the "line of fire" for risk of damage.

I quickly made my operative plans. I instructed the anesthetist to put the operating table in the Trendelenburg position, which meant to tilt the table so the patient's head would be lower than his feet to bring more blood to the most important parts of the body, the brain and heart. I promptly took a scalpel, made an incision in the abdomen and honed-in on the two most likely structures to cause life-threatening bleeding, the aorta, and the inferior vena cava.

Luckily the bleeding was venous and not arterial. I spotted a puncture hole in the abdominal portion of the inferior vena cava. Once identified and isolated, it was easy to repair. I stopped the bleeding by initially applying manual pressure and using a vascular clamp to partially occlude the vessel. I then placed a few sutures to repair the perforation and removed the clamp to re-establish blood flow. The patient was transfused with several units of blood and the surgeon of record closed the abdominal incision. I left the room approximately twenty minutes after entering. The patient survived and did well.

I knew what to do because I had encountered similar injuries of abdominal vessels during my general surgery and trauma training at Grady Memorial Hospital. Graduates of my program had each performed several hundred abdominal explorations during their training. We were all on top of our game in managing abdominal and chest trauma.

A second even more interesting case occurred when I was completing an operation in another country. The operating room head nurse rushed into my room informing me that I was needed right away to repair an iatrogenic (doctor-caused) vascular injury. I replied, "Sure, happy to help." He said, "It's in a small community hospital a few miles away, so we need to leave right away with our vascular equipment."

We jumped into an ambulance, went to the other hospital, and were quickly guided into the operating room. Within minutes, I had assessed the situation and made my action plan. Based on the description the surgeon had given me regarding the direction he attempted entry into the abdominal cavity, I had my suspicions of what had happened.

From his description and my understanding and expert knowledge of human anatomy, I knew exactly what he most likely had injured. I made an abdominal incision, gained control of the abdominal aorta proximally, found the bleeding in the right iliac artery, applied a partial occluding clamp, repaired the artery and re-established flow to the right leg. There was a small perforation in the inferior vena cava, which I repaired, too.

A year or so later my wife and I were attending a wedding when a young couple stopped by to greet us. It was that patient and her husband. It was gratifying to see that she had made full recovery.

Early in my medical career, I had thought I wanted to be a neurosurgeon. That after having spent three years working on my doctor of philosophy in neurosciences at Emory University prior to medical school. I spent much of my summer vacations working with the chief of Neurosurgery at Emory Hospital. Being in the operating room at a young age watching skulls being opened, brain tumors and blood clots removed, and spinal surgeries to remove discs was amazing. Microscopes were being used for the first time in the country to perform operations on the brain through the nose to remove tumors of the pituitary gland. Few people at the age of twenty-five had such great opportunities. It was very exciting and I knew how fortunate I was to be witnessing these innovative surgeries.

At that time, I thought brain surgery was the "smart" thing to do. As time went by, my interests changed. As a neurosurgery resident rotating in general surgery at Grady Hospital, one day I was paged to the office of the Chairman of Surgery, Dr. W. Dean Warren. This wasn't a call a resident would normally want to get. I hurriedly answered the call only to have Chairman Warren telling me that he had gotten positive reports about my performance and was offering me a job in general surgery, "guaranteed" to lead to the prestigious chief resident position. Without thinking much about it, I said, "Yes, sir."

By that time, I had realized that my liking of general surgery exceeded neurosurgery. Such was apparently evident not only to me, but also to my faculty. But then, I had to make the painful call to the Chief of Neurosurgery informing him that I was withdrawing from his program. He never let me forget it either.

It takes many years of hard studying to become a physician and to graduate from medical school with an M.D. degree. Then if you want to become a surgeon, it seems like you start all over again with another several years of rigorous training to learn how to operate and become a qualified surgeon. If you want to become a cardiovascular surgeon, then you must spend another two to three additional years of specialized training to master operating on the heart and blood vessels. Each time you want to subspecialize, you will need to spend extra time training. Every time you decide to try a new procedure, you'll need to study, be mentored, trained, and proctored, in order to perform the procedure safely. The learning process in surgery is never-ending. That is how it should be, always learning and sharpening one's surgical skills. Learning new techniques and making operations safer for our patients, reducing risks, and improving outcomes should be the goals of every surgeon.

Surgery is a challenging profession. It's a highly visible, high-risk career. Operating on adults is challenging, but operating on children is far more challenging by several orders of magnitude.

I have tremendous respect for congenital surgeons, particularly those in my subspecialty. Congenital heart diseases are much different and more complex than adult heart diseases, putting aside the obvious size differences and all the complexities brought into the mix. The different disease entities that are unique to newborn babies and children make congenital cardiac disorders, and how to correct them, significantly more challenging and demanding. Congenital heart surgeons stand at the pinnacle of the pyramid of heart surgery.

In addition to the above, there's an emotional layer makes work on babies and children so much more demanding, yet rewarding at the same time. In my training, I spent almost an entire year working with my mentor Professor Willis Williams, Chief of Congenital Cardiac Surgery at Emory. He took a special interest in my education and training. He was a great teacher, educator, role model, and a dear friend.

He worked relentlessly for his patients, caring for every single one of them as if they were his own children. He taught me how to patch different types of holes in the heart (atrial and ventricular defects), how to close patent ductus arteriosus, how to perform Glenn shunts, how to repair pectus excavatum, and the list goes on. Everything I know about pediatric heart surgery, I learned from Dr. Williams. His teachings paid off then and continue to pay off to this day.

On Dr. Williams' service, I worked with boundless energy. I did so, first and foremost, because sick babies and children intimidated me. I was terrified that something would happen to a child on my watch or while I was operating on one of them. When I was on call, I would immediately leave my call room anytime a nurse summoned me on any issue regarding a juvenile patient. I would check the patient out from head to toe just to be sure he or she was okay.

Before starting the rotation on the congenital cardiac surgery, I had thoughts of wanting to become a specialist in that discipline. By the end of my rotation, as you will read later, that idea departed me for good. The thought of a child dying on my watch was constantly on my mind. The image of a mom crying from the loss of a child where I was involved with its case was terrifying to me. It was almost a pathological phobia that ultimately dissuaded me from pursuing a career in congenital heart surgery.

During my rotation there, my first child, Rashid, was about ten months old. Every day when I got home after a long day at the hospital, he would jump into my lap and go for my shirt pocket grabbing the ink pens from their usual place. Rashid was a very active child. He was always very playful, demanding attention and wanting to spend playtime with me after not seeing me for couple of days while I was on call in the hospital.

I became accustomed to my son Rashid grabbing pens out of my shirt pocket every evening when I came home. He grabbed them and I snatched them back. And so, we would play, back and forth. Rashid was fascinated with this game, as if he had discovered something unique.

Being a second-year cardiac surgery resident on the congenital service was similar to being the lowest man on the totem pole again. I had to write progress notes on patients in the morning, check all labs, review all X-rays, first assist in the operating room and at the end of a long day, get consent forms signed by parents of children who were to undergo cardiac procedures the following day.

I worked four months on that service, on call every third night, typically spending the night in the hospital taking care of fresh post-open-heart kids. Some were newborn children who'd had complex heart surgeries that had to be done at their very young ages, while others were a little older, but still young children who had had various forms of cardiac defects corrected.

Operating on adults had its own sets of challenges, but operating on children had additional challenges. Not only was the science much more complex, but the calculations had to be much more exact. We couldn't estimate dosages of medications without difficulty, as we often did for adults. In children, there was no room for miscalculations. With the small size of children, a few percentage points off and you were way off target and would have completely missed the therapeutic window. More important was the psychological factor of dealing with children. For me, taking care of sick children was quite an emotional experience. Every child was a world within himself or herself. He or she was a world, a future--and with a career to be made. Each child was the focal point of the entire family. Every child was a universe in his or her own right. All of us felt that way, and we were all very protective of our patients, like our own children.

One evening, I was getting the "operative consents" for the following day's operations and went into a child's room. He was scheduled for an aortic root reconstructive procedure.

The child was about my son's age. No sooner than I went into his room to speak with his mom to explain the operation, the risks involved, the potential benefits, and the complications when the child jumped into my lap. He grabbed the pens out of my shirt pocket, exactly like my son did at home every night. That was a moment I will never forget. To this day, almost thirty years later, I can see the face of that child in my mind's eye. I can still see his blond hair, blue eyes, and fair skin. The mom signed the consent form and I walked away. That child left such an impression on me that I have carried his image with me since.

The next day, I was in the operating room early, waiting for the child to be brought in for his scheduled procedure. The image of him jumping up in my lap and grabbing the pens kept coming back in my mind, reminding me again of my own son. The child was prepared for the operative procedure. All the arterial lines, intravenous lines, various monitoring lines, cables, and instruments were placed, along with the endotracheal tube. The skin was scrubbed, prepped, and covered with sterile towels and drapes. Dr. Williams and I started the operation and he made a skin incision on the little chest to gain access to the heart and aorta. He would repair a narrowing in the origin of the aorta as it came out from the heart.

So, we started the procedure. We carefully opened the breastbone, followed by opening the pericardium. Heparin, a blood thinner, was given by vein to allow the placing of the patient on the heart lung machine, followed by inserting special tubes into the aorta and right atrium. The patient was placed on cardiopulmonary bypass, and his heart stopped by applying a clamp to aorta and administering a special medication containing potassium. We then opened the narrowed aorta and carefully examined it.

Once we opened the aorta and looked at it from inside, we realized how narrow it was. Luckily the valve itself was free of disease, was fully functional, and didn't need to be replaced. The blockage was limited to the wall of the aorta itself, immediately distal to the aortic valve, thus making the job a little easier, or so we thought at that moment. To enlarge the "root" of the aorta, we had to patch the area of narrowing with a synthetic material that we would tailor to the shape and size needed. Accordingly, we fitted that patch into the desired shape, size, and location and sewed it in.

In cardiac surgery, there are certain things we study and learn as basic scientific principles and certain things that are "arts of the profession that you learn by seeing." Reading an EKG is a science. Shaping a patch into an aorta is more of an art than a science. You must learn it more by seeing it and developing an "eye" for it rather than memorizing specific formulas.

So, we looked at the narrowing and figured how to enlarge it. We asked for a sterile, synthetic patch, shaped a small piece of it to the size we desired, and began to sew it in place. The patch was made from Dacron, a polyester material commonly used to repair or replace blood vessels.

We sewed the patch in place and immediately the aorta became larger. It looked like we eliminated the hourglass-shaped narrowing that was causing difficulty for blood to flow out of the heart. To our eyes, all looked great. We took the cross clamp off the aorta to allow blood to flow back into the coronary arteries and for the heart to regain function—to start beating again and to regain activity. The heart started to warm up, began to contract and soon took over the function of the heart lung machine. We were ready to come off bypass. The EKG looked good and the blood pressure normalized. All systems looked good so, we came off the heart-lung machine.

We waited for few minutes before removing the tubes from the heart and everything seemed normal. The tubes were removed and we gave protamine to reverse the heparin we had employed to use with the heart-lung machine.

As we started to close the chest, something very alarming began happening. The heart started to slow down. The heart rate that was stable in the nineties started dropping down into the eighties, seventies, sixties and then fifties. We immediately connected the pacemaker wires to the pacemaker and turned it on. The pacemaker would not capture and the heart stopped completely. It started to swell and the blood pressure dropped precipitously. Suddenly, we had no blood pressure or heart rate. To say panic hit the operating room would be a giant understatement. In the span of less than a minute, the case went from normal blood pressure, normal EKG, and "ready to close the chest," to full cardiac arrest—for unknown reasons! All in less than 60 seconds, more likely 20 or 30 seconds, although at the time it felt like a lifetime of fear, uncertainty, chaos, pain, and agony.

The anesthesiologist was pushing epinephrine in the central venous lines trying to get the heart to "kick-in" again and to pharmacologically raise the blood pressure. Dr. Williams started open massage on the small, swollen and "dead" heart. He gave the order to infuse a big bolus of heparin to go back on bypass to support the circulation and resuscitate the child. As we were doing so, I shared with Dr. Williams what I was thinking as we were facing a life or death situation. I said, "We need to take the Dacron patch out and replace it with a softer bovine patch." As I recall, he looked at me with bewilderment in his eyes.

I stated with confidence, "The patch must have kinked the left main. That is the only explanation for what happened." With great humility, he accepted my observation and proceeded to do what I had suggested. Soon we were back on bypass.

He cross-clamped the aorta again and gave a dose of cardioplegia solution into the aorta. He took down the old repair and started to redo the entire operation again. He took out the Dacron patch and replaced it with a soft and pliable bovine one. We closed the aorta again and removed the cross clamp. The heart was re-perfused with warm, oxygenated blood, and the heart began working again with great vigor, as if nothing had happened. The blood pressure and EKG normalized again and stayed that way. We came off bypass and closed the chest. The child was taken to the intensive care unit and extubated a few hours later.

The little boy, who played with my pens the night before, just like my son did, went home a few days later. I completed my services at Children's Hospital having decided not to pursue a career in pediatric cardiac surgery. To this day, I'm still intimidated by children and their health issues.

Willis Williams was a great teacher and a remarkable congenital heart surgeon who taught generations of heart surgeons and treated thousands of children. Thank you, Willis, for all you have done for me and for my patients.

CHAPTER TEN

"Dr. Lattouf, You'd Better Not Kill This Baby's Mom"
What Left a Heart Surgeon Speechless

It was a Saturday evening in the spring of 2014 when my wife and I met three other couples for dinner. The host was a VIP international patient upon whom I had performed a complex, high-risk heart operation a year earlier. I had been on vacation in my hometown in Jordan when he had developed sudden chest pain, was hospitalized, and underwent a heart catheterization. His able cardiologist confirmed that two of the previous bypasses from 18 years earlier had once again become blocked, causing his heart attack.

This patient was a childhood friend of my older brother, where they had gone to school together from kindergarten through college. Since then, he had served in very high governmental and diplomatic positions in Jordan. His condition was unstable and he needed immediate heart surgery. He couldn't possibly fly to the United States where he had his first operation almost two decades earlier. So, with two of my colleague surgeons assisting, I spent 10 hours in the operating room working on him. The outcome was very good and his operation was successful.

A few days later, I made the long plane ride back to Atlanta. For follow-up in the immediate post-operative period, my colleagues and I relied on "home-made" telemedicine equipment to check on his wound and review his vital signs. We jointly reviewed his X-rays and discussed his other medical issues.

After his complete recovery, he came to Atlanta for another post-operative visit and further evaluation. All was well, and in celebration of his good health, he hosted a dinner in one of Atlanta's finest Italian restaurants. As we were about to be seated, my phone rang. It was the hospital operator informing me that I was needed for emergency surgery on a 35-year-old woman who was 36 weeks pregnant and having both chest and abdominal pains. "But I'm not an OB (obstetrician) doc!" I said.

"Well, let me put you through to the ER doc who wants to speak with you."

The ER doctors told me, "She has an aortic dissection (a tear within the wall of a blood vessel) and is having labor pains at the same time.".

"Are you sure?" I asked.

"I have the CTA (chest CT scan with angiographic dye) and it shows massive Type A dissection, extending from the aortic valve, through the arch and all the way down to the abdominal aorta. And yes, she is in labor."

"Please send me the images as I need to review the CTA right away!"

I had to see the images with my own eyes, and started making a series of very complex plans. I received the images and the dissection was indeed extensive. To make things even more critical, there was blood leaking from the torn aorta into the space around the heart. The patient could die at any moment. We had to race against time before the aorta blew out completely or the heart stopped from blood causing pressure on its chambers.

I asked the ER doctor to immediately summon a helicopter and have the patient flown to my hospital for emergency, life-saving procedures. I called my operating room team, cardiac anesthesia team, high-risk OB surgeons, and neonatal critical care specialist, requesting them to immediately head to the operating room. One operating room was readied without delay for the pregnant mom and a second nearby was converted into newborn, high-risk recovery room with highly specialized incubator, monitors, ventilators, and other unique, neonatal equipment.

I left my party and headed to the hospital, expecting the patient to arrive about the same time as I did, and then I'd take her straightaway to life-saving surgery. When I reached the operating room, she wasn't there! I waited a few minutes and when she still hadn't shown up, I called the referring hospital and asked to speak to the doctor. I questioned, "Where's my patient?"

"She's still here," explained the ER doctor. "The air ambulance pilot is refusing to take her on his helicopter! He says he cannot take a pregnant woman on his chopper."

"Please allow me to speak with him," I impatiently requested. The pilot came on the line and I stated rather demandingly, "Sir, please immediately fly this lady to my hospital. If you do not, I will hold you personally responsible if she dies."

Minutes later, the chopper landed on my hospital's roof.

The patient, a very attractive blond with her hair made up beautifully, was rolled in on a stretcher to my operating room. She explained, "I was at the hairdresser when I felt the chest pain. I called my husband and told him about the sudden pain. He told me, 'You better immediately go straight to the ER and get checked out.'"

Now in my operating room, she was readied for anesthesia as dozens of doctors, nurses, and support staff prepared to proceed with two high-risk operations: a C-section to deliver the baby and a complex heart operation on the mom. It was imperative that the life-threatening aortic tear be repaired and bleeding around the heart controlled before either went out of control or caused immediate stroke or death. Everyone was aware of the risks. We all knew what we were up against, knowing that this highly complex operation could result in a mortality rate of 200%. A major issue in operating on pregnant women and using general anesthesia is that anesthetic medications might rapidly get into the baby's blood stream, slow or stop the baby's breathing, and slow down the heart rate, putting its life in real danger.

I was very nervous and so was everyone else in the operating room. Thus, as soon as the mom went to sleep, the high-risk OB doctors would have only a few minutes to make the abdominal incision, open the uterus, pull the baby out, and hand her to the neonatal intensive care doctor.

With military precision, the young mom was quickly prepped and draped while two gowned and gloved surgical teams were ready for action. The mom was given the anesthetic medication and in literally only three minutes, the baby was out. The tiny girl arrived screaming at the top of her lungs. She came out fully alert and healthy-looking with very strong lungs and voice. The two-dozen health care workers were each working intensely and silently completing their assigned tasks. The room was quiet except for the infant's cries. She was screaming as if wanting to announce her arrival to the world. No one whispered a single word.

The voice of the crying baby created a new reality. We were all intimidated by the newborn baby who was only minutes old. We felt her immense power and it gave me a feeling that I had never experienced before or since.

The OB doctors closed the incision and I hurriedly made mine by opening the breastbone using a special surgical sternal saw.

As I started to evacuate the blood from around the heart, I ordered heparin to place her on the heart lung machine. Sofia, my able anesthesiologist, raised her head above the sterile drapes and in a loud and commanding voice heard by everyone in the room said, "Dr. Lattouf, you'd better not kill this baby's mom."

I was stunned that she would make such a statement at that very moment. I couldn't and didn't respond. Suddenly I felt a pain in my gut. I was shaken by the tension of the moment and the immense responsibility of caring for the future of a newborn baby and a young mom's life.

I was approaching mental anguish and was afraid for the baby and her mom. In the very depth of my soul, I was afraid of failure. I was truly afraid of what Dr. Sofia was warning me not to do; I had no alternatives. I could not back out. It was the most anxious moment of my career. More likely, the most anxious moment of my life!

I knew at that moment there was one powerful person in the room, only one. It was the newborn baby girl. Despite her utter weakness and total dependence on us, she was still the most powerful one in the room and owned the moment. She had the future and we were there to rightfully serve and protect her and protect her interest in a future with her own mom.

I knew that I was no match for this newborn. In front of a jury, no matter what the circumstances were, she would win the day. That baby girl was the most powerful person I had ever encountered. She had over-powered me. I gave in and recognized that she was the master of the moment.

I knew my job and it wasn't only to perform a highly complex heart operation under very unusual circumstances. It wasn't simply to repair and replace the damaged valves and arteries of this new mom's heart, but it was much more personal. I had to protect and save the mom so the newborn girl would grow up in her mother's arms, be taken to school by her, and grow up to become a teenager who would attend her high school prom under her mom's watchful eyes.

For me to let the mother die, in my hands and under my watch, wasn't an option. I made up my mind to do the impossible and give the baby her rightful chance to grow up with her mom's care, attention, and love, not unlike my own daughters.

In my twenty-five year career of heart surgery, I have performed many high-risk and complex heart operations, but this one was unique. I had never done an aortic root replacement, valve replacement, re-implantation of the coronary arteries, replacement of the entire aortic arch and proximal descending aorta, and re-implanting the arteries supplying the brain and arms, all in one setting on a pregnant woman. As I found out later, it wasn't just my first operation of this kind—this complex operation had never before been reported in the medical literature.

For the next ten hours, my team and I worked diligently repairing and replacing torn heart and aortic tissue.

By nine o'clock the next morning and after many hundreds of stitches, the woman's heart was beating forcefully and I closed the chest. I escorted both of my patients to their respective ICU beds. Fatigued and mentally exhausted, I left for home.

During the operation, I painfully rehearsed in my mind what Dr. Sofia had said at the beginning of the operation, "Do not kill this baby's mom." I had been terrified. As Sofia's words kept reverberating in my mind, I had decided that if my patient didn't survive, I would resign as heart surgeon. This would have been my last operation. I couldn't imagine killing that baby's mom and yet continuing to face my colleagues with the burden of a newborn child orphaned due to my failure. I couldn't have imagined being able to live with such shame.

I arrived home totally exhausted, and slept for the next six hours. My wife later told me that she had never seen me so exhausted—and speechless. Later that afternoon, I went back to the hospital to see my patient. She had no further bleeding and her blood pressure was stable. Her blood oxygen level was excellent and she was making good urine. All was well, except she had sudden onset of seizures. Her head, arms and legs were shaking uncontrollably. The intensivist (the ICU physician) was worried that she might have sustained severe brain damage during the operation. Poor blood supply to the brain is known to cause seizures after complex heart operations. He was fearful that poor oxygen delivery to the brain was the reason for the seizure. This would have been disastrous.

Defiantly, I said, "No way. I gave her the best brain protection throughout the long and difficult operation. I monitored her brain oxygen level every minute, so it must be something else causing the seizures." I recalled from my medical school days 25 years earlier, a condition called perinatal eclampsia, a very rare occurrence that may happen around delivery time. I remembered learning that treatment of this rare, seizure-producing condition is simply giving magnesium sulfate. I said to my intensive care doctor, "Let's give her two grams of magnesium intravenously."

The magnesium was given, the seizures halted, and few hours later the patient woke up. She was then weaned off the ventilator and, upon examination, found to be neurologically intact. We treated her high blood pressure and the seizures never occurred again.

Once fully wake, she asked for her newborn baby. For the first time, the mom and her baby were re-united.

A year later, my patient, her husband, the baby, and their three-year-old daughter came to see me in my office. The one-year-old baby was beautiful: blond, fair-skinned, and full of life. Mom was healthy and looked great. Dad and sister were in great spirits and happy to have their family intact.

And I didn't give up my job.

One year later, after the operation and baby delivery

CHAPTER ELEVEN

The One Sentence that Saved My Career

Friends in Many Places

C ardiac surgery is a complex and high-risk business. The patients are often older, usually very sick, and have multiple medical problems. The corrective surgery procedure is extremely complex. Such surgeries require large incisions, lengthy operations, infusion of many medications, and several days in the hospital under close observation. Very few heart surgeons go through their careers without encountering one or more malpractice lawsuits against them. Fortunately, most end up getting cleared in court, but only after great psychological and material cost.

A dozen years ago, I faced one painful malpractice case filed against me. It had an unusual ending. It was unusual for many reasons, none of which I could have predicted at the outset or during the lawsuit.

It was the case of an older gentleman in his mid-seventies who needed an aortic valve replacement for severe aortic stenosis and four-vessel coronary artery bypass grafting. I reviewed the heart cath and discussed the clinical details with the referring cardiologist and spoke at length with the patient and his married adult daughter. The operation was scheduled and successfully performed the following day.

The patient spent one day in the intensive care unit, made good progress, and moved to a private room. Gradually he began eating, drinking, walking the hallways without assistance, and using the bathroom without difficulty. All vital signs were normal: no fever, no atrial fibrillation, good oxygenation, and normal blood pressure.

On day six, as I was making my morning rounds, I visited the patient and spoke with him and his daughter. He seemed well and had no complaints. She asked me, "Can I take my dad home today? He seems to be doing well."

We checked his chest X-ray and it was clear. His lab results were normal, except for his white blood cell count, which was barely above normal. It was 11.4 with upper level normal for non-operative patients being 11.2. With the patient having no fever, no cough, and a clear chest X-ray, I wasn't concerned about the marginally elevated WBC.

Accordingly, I instructed the daughter to monitor her dad's daily temperature, check his wound, and keep an eye out for any productive cough with yellow, green, or brown mucus. Those were my usual instructions to all my patients and their families at time of discharge. I instructed her that if he developed any of the above or if she had any concerns at all, to call us. She could then bring her dad back to the hospital or take him to the nearest emergency room. She expressed her understanding and thanked me for providing the surgical care for her dad. She accompanied her father as he was discharged that afternoon.

A couple of weeks later, I got a call from one of my hospital internists asking me to see a patient in my hospital office and review his chest X-ray. We discussed the need to place a chest tube in his left side to relieve a collection of fluid that was noted on the X-ray. I went to see the patient, reviewed his medical file, and found that the patient in question was one on whom I had operated a couple of weeks earlier. He had a fever and had consolidation in his left lower lobe, in addition to left-sided pleural effusion suggesting a para-pneumonic effusion. So, I obtained consent from the patient and his daughter and placed a chest tube in the left pleural space and drained several hundred milliliters of cloudy fluid from the chest. A sample was sent to the lab for culture and sensitivity in accordance with protocol. The patient was already on antibiotic coverage.

Every day, I went by to see the patient and closely monitored his progress. A couple of days later, I noticed that the lower portion of the sternal wound had started to turn red and was draining purulent fluid. This was bad news as it meant that the parapneumonic effusion and pneumonia had secondarily infected my surgical incision. Thus, I consulted plastic surgery in anticipation that the patient would require a reconstructive procedure. This was typically done by rotating the chest and/or abdominal wall muscle into the infected area, as healthy muscle has the ability to fight infection and speed up wound healing.

The plastic surgeon spoke with the patient and his daughter, obtained consent and proceeded to perform the required procedure in the operating room the next day. The procedure went well, but a couple of days later, part of the skin suture of the new incision was looking loose and leaking fluid. It warranted another trip to the operating room for dressing change and minor wound revision.

The plastic surgeon spoke with the daughter and requested permission to operate. To his surprise, she declined. He called and asked me to speak with the daughter and try to convince her to allow him to perform the minor wound revision. I went to the intensive care unit, examined the wound myself and spoke with the daughter. I explained that I supported the plastic surgeon's request and strongly recommended that she permit him to make the necessary surgical revision.

The daughter came back with a stunning reply. She said, "No, I don't want my dad to have any more operations. He has had enough!" I countered, "But his wound will not heal and will continue to break down further. His new valve is at risk of getting infected and he would die if not aggressively treated." She insisted on not allowing the plastic surgeon to take her dad back into the operating room. Reluctantly, I conveyed the message to the plastic surgeon. We both agreed to perform local dressing changes, continue antibiotic coverage, and re-examine the wound the following day.

The next day, I came back and re-examined his wound. It wasn't looking good. In fact, it was opening up even more. It became clear to me that surgical repair was a must or else his condition would rapidly deteriorate and he would probably die from the infection. I went back again to plead with the daughter and her husband to allow us to revise the wound. She was adamant and again, refused. She made another drastic demand that made me angry. She said, "Doctor, my dad has had enough. Please give him a dose of morphine and take him off the ventilator!"

Hearing what she said, I nearly fell on the floor!

In my thirty-some-odd years of practicing medicine, I had never had anyone ask me to euthanize another human being, let alone a parent.

I said, "Your father is totally salvageable and can survive this hospitalization. His condition is not fatal." She replied, "He has had enough. I don't want him to have another surgery." I told her that there was no way that I would consent to her request as it went against every principle of my medical oath. I offered to transfer her father's care to another physician, but I would not carry out her request. With nothing else to discuss, I walked away.

I went directly to the nurse's station, pulled the patient's chart and entered in my own handwriting, the date and the time of 3:50 pm. I wrote, 'I have requested from the patient's daughter permission to allow plastic surgeon to revise the wound. She refused. She asked me to give her father morphine and discontinue the ventilator and I refused." I then dated and signed the entry. The patient's nurse entered a note in the chart stating that I had counseled the family about further surgical care and it was declined.

That was on Friday afternoon so I went home for the weekend. I came back on Monday to check on the patient and his room was empty. I inquired about what had happened and was told that the daughter asked a doctor to give her dad morphine and remove the breathing tube. That was done, the patient died and was taken to a funeral home.

I felt anger and helplessness. I told myself that it was too late and I had done everything I could. I had no control over the situation. Now in retrospect, maybe I should have done more, such as asking for an "Ethics Consult" on Friday afternoon. But that hadn't occurred to me at the time.

Eighteen months or so later, my wife called me to tell me that a deputy sheriff had dropped off paperwork for a lawsuit in my name. Not knowing what this was all about, I went home that evening to read the served legal documents. Indeed, it read 'The Estate of XXXX vs. Dr. Omar Lattouf and the names of my hospital, clinic, university, an outlying hospital and the names of a half-dozen other doctors.' I sat down and read the complaint and was puzzled by it. I said to myself, "Why would

I be sued when I begged the woman to allow me to help her father get the needed surgical care? She wanted me to end his life and I had strongly objected and flatly refused to do what she had asked. She proceeded to find someone else to do the work for her and now she is blaming me for the death of her father! This didn't make any sense."

I was extremely distraught. I felt that all the hard work doctors do for their patients sometimes end up getting them nothing but pain and agony. It was heart breaking for me. I was both angry and saddened by the accusations.

I went through the medical record of the patient, word for word, repeatedly, trying to find any weak points in my case. I couldn't find any and then came the deposition. A female lawyer, along with my lawyer assigned to me by the university went through the deposition together. I was already provided with relevant information from the other hospital named in the lawsuit. The information from the other hospital was very insightful. I learned that a few days after his discharge from my hospital, that the patient had difficulty sleeping and hadn't been feeling well.

His daughter took him to a local emergency room where an ER nurse and physician examined him. Documentation revealed that his vital signs, chest X-rays, lack of a fever and other findings from his physical exam were reported as normal. The ER sheet actually had a pre-printed "smiley face" on it, indicating that all was well. The patient was given a prescription for a sedative to help him sleep and discharged.

The records further indicated that a couple of days later the patient was brought back to the same ER, this time coughing and with a fever. Chest X-rays this time revealed a small collection of fluid in the left lower lobe of the lungs, suggestive of pneumonia. He was admitted and started on antibiotics.

After spending a few more days there without making any substantial progress, he was transferred to my hospital. He was admitted to the medicine service and was treated for a few more days. Once a CT scan was done and confirmed a moderate sized collection of fluid was seen, I was asked to see him. Thus, I became involved with him again.

As I gave my deposition, the details of my encounters with the patient and family began coming back to me. I recalled the note I had written in the chart Friday afternoon at 3:50 pm and the conversation that I had with the daughter and her husband. I went through the chart, one page at a time looking for that note, but couldn't find it. I nearly went crazy looking through the paper medical record, repeatedly. I must have gone through every page a dozen times, but still couldn't find it.

Then came more bad news. The first was that a famous malpractice attorney had joined the junior female attorney on the other "team." This new attorney ("TR") had a reputation for being very convincing with the jury, always on the plaintiff's side of malpractice suits against physicians and hospitals. He was tall, handsome, and very well-spoken in court. He was well known to be very prepared for his court cases, always. This new attorney was a "top-rated" lawyer in every way.

More bad news was that the other hospital decided to 'settle out of court.' The rest of the doctors from hospital were dropped from the case one after the other, leaving me as the only physician left to fend for myself. By this point, I was frightened, but still angry. I was wondering why I was left alone in this case. I was about to face one of the most formidable medical malpractice attorneys in the country with a reputation that was feared by the strongest institutions and their physicians. I returned to the medical records department for I knew that I had to find my hand-written note if I had any chance of surviving this ordeal.

It occurred to me that back in those days, at the time of every patient discharge the paper medical record was immediately taken down to the Medical Records Department to make a film record (called a medical microfiche) of each page. I asked the director of the department to pull the patient's "microfiche" for me and she did. I loaded it on the viewer and went through it one page at a time. Sure enough, I found the one and only missing page with my hand-written note. I couldn't believe my eyes. I went running to the director and asked her to make me several paper copies of that page. I placed one page in my clinic office, one in my home office, one in my safe, and one in my hospital locker. I didn't want to take any chances of losing this important document. As the court date approached, I shared a copy with my attorneys and asked them to make it available to be used as an exhibit in the court during my testimony and cross-examination.

Spending two solid weeks in court was one of the most painful experiences I have ever been through. I had to cancel all my clinics, appointments, and scheduled surgeries to be in court from 8:00 am until 5:00 pm. Sitting through all the proceedings, including jury selection, was physically and psychologically exhausting.

Then came the plaintiff's presentation. The daughter described her dad in great detail: his years as a young man who served in the Navy, the things he liked to do, and so forth. She did a great job creating a real-life image of the deceased patient.

The following day was my turn to testify and be cross-examined. My two very able attorneys did an excellent job educating me about the law and how I should conduct myself in court. I was to be specific in giving my answers and respectful in every way. They told me not to go into unnecessary details and to stick to only the questions that were asked.

During many of our conversations, I told my senior attorney that I was innocent. Why would they accuse me of killing this poor man when I did everything in my power to save his life? I said, "It was his daughter who killed him, as she wanted me to give him morphine and discontinue the ventilator so he could stop breathing and die. Both times she asked, I flatly refused."

My attorney said, "You'd better not mention that his daughter killed him as the jury would not take kindly to that statement." I said, "What the hell do you expect me to say? She did ask me to end his life and here is my documentation!"

My attorney's face turned red as he said, "You'd better not say that or you'll regret it." I shot back, maybe foolishly, but said, "I will say exactly that. If I'm going to jail, I will do it on my terms, not yours." My attorney was angry and so was I. We rode in his car to court that morning, neither one talking to the other. I was called to the stand, was sworn-in, and had my first encounter with the plaintiff's attorney.

Standing in front of me in court, he seemed like an imposing giant. He started asking me questions and I crafted my answers with very carefully selected words. He then displayed a huge poster board, about six by eight feet, with a graph showing that on the day of discharge the white blood count was 11.4. Several days later it had risen to 17.

He asked me this question: "What was the WBC of the patient on day of discharge?"

I replied, "11.4."

He asked, "What was upper normal WBC in your lab?"

I said, "For a normal, healthy individual 11.2."

He said, "Please be specific in answering my question. What is upper normal in your lab?"

I replied with same answer with an explanation that normal ranges are done on healthy people and not on post-open heart patients. In my judgment, a 0.2 difference was not significant."

The judge surprised me when he said, "Please be specific in your answer to the question." "Yes sir," I said.

Then the attorney pointed to the chart and said, "Your patient was discharged with an elevated WBC and several days later the WBC was 17, thus indicating that you had missed an infection when he was discharged! You failed your patient and you caused his death by failing to diagnose his pneumonia at the time of discharge."

I replied, "No sir. When I saw him last in my hospital, he had no fever, no productive cough, was walking well, verbalized no complaints, and I gave full instructions to him and his daughter on what to look for and what to do in case of new symptoms."

I further said, "Look at the ER records from the other hospital. He had no fever and the chest X-ray was reported as clear. He was even sent home with a smiley face circle on his chart so the nurse and doctor were not concerned about him and didn't see any pneumonia. So how can you accuse me of killing this patient? I did my job well and did everything in my power to save his life. I even pleaded with his daughter to allow the plastic surgeon to revise the wound, but she refused."

The plaintiff's attorney said, "What are you suggesting here?"

I asked for my handwritten note to be put up for the jury to view. I said, "Here is my handwritten note stating that I had asked permission for wound revision and was denied. His daughter requested that I give her father morphine intravenously and discontinue the ventilator to let her dad die. I refused her request."

I further stated, "I came back Monday morning and found that the patient had died after being given intravenous morphine and having the ventilator withdrawn, honoring her request."

The attorney asked, "Could you point to that person in the room?" I pointed my finger and said, "Yes, the lady with the blond hair, sitting there. She is the one who wanted her father to be given morphine, discontinue the ventilator, and let him die." That was the end of my cross-examination. It was about 5:00 pm and the judge adjourned court for the day.

I was emotionally fatigued when I walked out. My attorney was angry, as was I. He finally broke the silence and blurted out, "I instructed you not to say that." I looked him squarely in the face and said, "I told you I was going to say exactly that."

The next day, it was time for the daughter to be cross-examined. The junior defense attorney on my side was a sharp, young female attorney and did the cross examination on our team's behalf. As she went through the series of questions, she asked her if she had ever met Dr. Lattouf.

The lady answered in the affirmative.

She asked her if she remembered the conversation with Dr. Lattouf on the day of discharge. She could not recall the details, but seemed to recall that they had spoken that day.

The young attorney asked her if Dr. Lattouf had kept them informed about the care throughout the hospitalization period. Again, she answered in the affirmative.

The attorney asked if Dr. Lattouf was nice to her She answered, "Yes, he was."

Then came the killer question. "If Dr. Lattouf was nice to you, answered all your questions and cared for your dad, then why are you suing him?" the attorney asked.

"I didn't know that I was suing Dr. Lattouf! I thought I was suing the hospital," the daughter said.

The young attorney looked at the jury, then looked at the judge and said, "She didn't know she was suing Dr. Lattouf. Then who is she suing?"

The case went to the jury and they returned to the courtroom in only thirty minutes. The foreman of the jury remained standing and issued the verdict, in favor of the defense.

I stood up, thanked my attorney, and walked towards the jury box. I extended my hand to each one of the members and thanked them all. To my surprise, many of them said, "Doc, if my mother or father needed heart surgery, I would bring them to you!"

My attorney walked to our opponent's attorney, shook hands and we walked out to have a meal at a nearby restaurant. As we left the restaurant, I thanked my attorneys again for their excellent work and expressed my utmost gratitude for a job well done.

As we were each heading to our respective cars, I asked my senior attorney one final question, "Why did all the other doctors drop out and I was the only one left to defend in this case?"

He said, "We at the university's legal office studied the case and decided that if we let the other doctors to remain in, they might start saying the wrong things and get us into trouble. You have a reputation of being capable to defend your medical positions and we knew that you would not cower in front of TR. Thus, we decided to keep only you."

A couple of years went-by and I was talking with a business associate when he said, "I found out you know a good friend of mine!" I asked, "Who?" He said, "TR." I said, "That's one man I never want to see in court again."

A few months later, I needed some legal advice and thought TR would be the perfect lawyer to ask. I called his office and asked his secretary if she would allow me to speak to him. He was very gracious to accept my call. I told him I needed legal advice and that I had developed tremendous respect for him for the way he handled my court case. He was most kind and even invited me to lunch in his office. We had a very nice, friendly lunch, but didn't talk much business. At the end of lunch, he looked at me and said, "From here on in, you are my friend and I will never sue you." I thanked him and accepted his offer of friendship.

Since then, we have had many meetings, phone calls, Christmas cards, holiday gift exchanges and so on. I have sought his opinion on complex legal issues and he has been most helpful in many ways. He trusted my opinions on medical issues important to him, too.

Recently, he called to share some important personal information. He made a point to say, "Although we were introduced to one another in a difficult situation, you have become one whom I consider a dear and trusted friend"

I said, "I feel the same way about you and consider you a dear and trusted friend, too."

CHAPTER TWELVE

It Took Twenty-Five Years to Accomplish, But We Did It
Nothing Good Happens Fast

I 've learned that some things take a long time to accomplish and I'm no stranger to long-term projects. My career as a practicing cardiac surgeon took me a total of twelve years of KG-1 through high school, another eighteen years of college, post-graduate education, and residency training. Add it all up and you have thirty-six years of schooling before I had a full-time job as a surgeon, earning a living and working at a real job.

This story is about something that has taken a lifetime to accomplish, but we finally did it. It all began in the late 1980s, as I began my practice in Atlanta, when the idea of providing consultations via computers and telephones occurred to me.

Being originally from Jordan with strong connections there, I often received calls from friends and family who had medical questions and needed some guidance. In order to give an expert opinion, I had to request the full medical file, including any imaging and lab studies that the patients had obtained. So had to mail bulky files and I often had to wait until other studies arrived before I could render an opinion. In the obvious absence of the patient, I needed as much information that was available to share with another specialist or to render an opinion of my own. This entire process took a considerable amount of time. Back then, there was no email and the Internet was known only in very limited circles—and certainly had not been opened to the public. Cell phones were called "car-phones" and came in a big bulky bag with the antenna installed outside the car. Instagram, Twitter, and Facebook (and their inventors) hadn't yet been born!

In early 1990, it occurred to me that someday, somehow, we could transfer entire patient files of text and images, including chest X-rays, CT scans, heart catheterizations, and even conversations between doctors and patients, across cities, countries or oceans. This process would let us exchange opinions via some sort of interactive means of where the patients and providers were located. At the time, those concepts were absolutely crazy ideas, but they were my dreams nonetheless. These ideas were way ahead of their time and few thought they were even achievable.

I had two primary objectives:

1. Relay live medical information across long distances in a cost-effective and interactive fashion to facilitate education. It wasn't practical that every time a hospital or a medical school wanted to invite an expert from the US to Jordan or another country that he or she had to fly for eighteen-hours each way at great expense in time and money. How do you justify these factors for a one-hour lecture? Surely one could argue that valuable relation-building meetings and other "fillers" could be packed into a trip to justify the cost in time and money. But, as the hardship of international travel has increased, the value of virtual presence has become even more important and cost effective.

2. The second objective was to allow clinical consultations between patients and doctors or between

health care providers from great distances. This would require the ability for both parties to be able to view lab tests and even to view, live, certain clinical studies or operative procedures. Example: a dermatologist in the US could see a patient's skin lesion from thousands of miles away and suggest treatment.

Those two objectives were tall orders in the early 1990s and it was then that I started dabbling in technology. It was an intriguing and interesting journey to have a young heart surgeon at the beginning of his career wanting to create a new system of communication in medicine. The idea occurred to me that doctors around the world would want to join a network in order to communicate with one another, and with experts in their medical fields of interest. My ideas morphed into a project that I called (at the time) the International Medical Institute (IMI), an organization to facilitate global telemedical communications.

I pulled addresses of surgeons from one of the societies that I belonged to and mailed hardcopy invites to several hundred of them. To my surprise, the rate of return was something like 105%! Some of the recipients had actually made copies of my invitation letters and forwarded them to their colleagues. They completed these and returned them to me. Having a very busy surgical schedule, I failed to recognize the importance of the messages that my colleagues were sending and the size of the business opportunity.

I continued to pursue technology development and attempted to build telemedicine stations made of computers connected to blood pressure machines, scanners, cameras, and scopes. I held meetings on telemedicine and its future in healthcare in the United States, Europe, and the Middle East. These meetings were academically interesting, but I didn't have a clear business plan on how to transform these initiatives into fundable and sustainable, money-making projects. These projects crashed big time, but before they did, there were lessons I learned and experiences well worth sharing.

By September 1994, we had quite an ongoing international initiative in telemedicine. There was major conference in Geneva, Switzerland, attended by representatives from ministries of health and universities in thirty-eight countries. International speakers included world-renowned heart surgeon Michael DeBakey, who traveled from Houston to Geneva to address the audience on his views on telemedicine and the work he was doing in the field.

Professor Jag Sheth, futurist and marketing guru, spoke about his vision of the intersection of technology, telecommunication, and remote diagnostics as a way to reduce the cost of health care for the masses. He predicted that at some point in the future, it would become more convenient and cost-effective for body fluid testing to be performed at home and the results reported via telephones instead of patients carrying the samples to a clinic or laboratory. My interest in telemedicine remained, but as time went by I had to make a decision between being a full-time heart surgeon providing care for my patients or dabbling in technology.

In 1990s, the cost of the bandwidth on the Internet was prohibitively high. To continue in the pursuit of telemedicine technology was costly and time consuming, more than I could afford. I kept my academic interest, but gave up my development and business interest. From time to time, I would go back and dabble a little with telemedicine technology, particularly as the cost of equipment and bandwidth dropped.

One summer, I went on a visit to my hometown of Amman, Jordan, with my wife Lina and our two daughters, Amal and Zeena. We had plans for a no-work vacation. We planned to go to the Dead Sea, Petra, and Aqaba—and just to enjoy ourselves. Amal and Zeena instructed me that I could not operate on this pleasure trip. Lina knew better, but stayed out of the conversation.

Sure enough, as soon as we arrived in Amman, my good friend and dear cardiology colleague called to inform me that a mutual friend, a former prime minister and senator, was hospitalized with unstable angina, awaiting a heart cath. He had had a coronary artery bypass operation twenty-years earlier. He was awaiting my arrival to perform the heart catheterization.

The following day, we did the cath and gathered to review the results. The group decision was that an emergency operation was necessary. He was too unstable to transfer to the US for me to operate on him there so we immediately took him to the operating room. So much for my non-working vacation!

Lina's prediction had come true. I began the complex operation with help from my two Jordanian colleagues; Dr. Asem and Dr. Hagob. I bypassed the diagonal and the right coronary artery (RCA), yet preserved the left internal mammary artery (LIMA) to the left anterior descending (LAD) artery. It was a full-day encounter and happily a successful procedure as well.

> *A bit of explanation: diagonal, RCA, and LAD arteries are branch arteries supplying blood to the heart muscle. When they block up with fatty growth, a heart attack happens. LIMA is an artery found on the back of breastbone that is used as a replacement for blocked coronary arteries that re-supply blood to heart muscle.*

While in Amman, I followed up with him on daily and he did very well. After his first day of recovery, my family and I were able to join up and visit the Dead Sea, Aqaba, and Petra. I spent the days with them, but drove back to be in Amman at night, just in case my patient needed me.

At the end of our vacation, I made my last visit to my patient prior to his discharge from the hospital. We headed to the airport and once we landed in Atlanta, I checked on him again by phone. Initially, he made good progress, but a few days later, his fever spiked. I asked my Amman cardiac surgeon colleagues to check on him, examine his wound and to report back to me. They did as I had asked and shared their concern that the lower part of the sternal incision was red and had some drainage.

I, too, became concerned. Wound infection, two weeks after heart surgery is a difficult and serious problem that can be life threatening if not managed well. Most often (and depending on the severity), these infections require further surgical intervention. At this point, the patient was at home so we advised him that he needed to be readmitted to the hospital for intravenous antibiotic therapy. He was adamant and insisted that he absolutely would not be readmitted as an inpatient under any circumstances.

He blamed his infection on the lack of attention by some of the healthcare providers at the hospital. Admittedly, infections that occur this soon after an operation are usually hospital-acquired. Generally, we don't know where the breakdown in sterility happens, and we often never find out. In his case, we had to immediately deal with this huge problem.

My challenge was how to treat my patient from across the Atlantic with the help of my two surgical colleagues who had assisted in the operative procedure. To begin with, we decided to convert his bedroom at home into a hospital room. We started an intravenous line and gave him the appropriate antibiotics twice daily. We obtained an outpatient CT scan of the chest, and it confirmed two fluid collections—one under the skin incision the length of the wound and another deep in the lower portion of the incision, extending deeper into the mediastinum, above the diaphragm.

The plan was to begin with antibiotics, open the skin wound and place a drain in the lower part of the incision. We would then assess whether decreases in fever and white blood count (WBC) indicated positive responses to our treatment. I really needed to see for myself, the wound and how it looked. So, we rigged a rudimentary, telemedicine system using an iPhone feature, Facetime. Every day my colleagues, Dr. Hagob and Dr. Asem, would change the dressing about mid-afternoon, Amman time, and while the dressing was opened, the iPhones would transmit images of the infected wound.

Gradually the upper part of the wound began showing signs of healing, but the lower part continued to drain. The patient continued to feel unwell, and continued having both a low-grade fever and elevated white blood count (WBC). That indicated retained, infected fluid. The fluid culture came back positive for infection and fortunately, the organisms were sensitive to our antibiotics. We kept the antibiotics flowing as scheduled.

In my Atlanta practice, I had frequently used a system called WoundVac; a silver-impregnated sponge placed on the wound and covered with airtight dressing, followed by connecting a vacuum system to the sponge. Thus, the sponge absorbs the fluid from the wound and the vacuum pulls the fluid out into an external canister.

We inquired to see such device was available in Jordan. Fortunately, we found something similar and applied it. But it failed to work, as the vacuum didn't have enough suction to draw the fluid from the depth of the wound. What should I do? My choices were to fly the patient to Atlanta or travel back to Amman and re-operate on him to fix his wound.

As usual, Lina was very supportive. She said, "If you need to fly back, do it. You must take care of your patient. Don't let anyone else operate on him."

Dr. Hagob and I decided to try one more thing before making a major decision to re-open the wound and do muscle flaps. We decided to take a small piece of a sterile, endotracheal suction catheter with an external diameter of about 3 millimeters and cut and use the distal 8 cm portion. We then placed a safety pin on the cut end and gently inserted the soft distal tip into the wound until it stopped. Next, we applied the silver-impregnated sponge on top of the pinned portion of the catheter, connected the vacuum tubing, applied the airtight dressing, and connected it to the external canister. Lastly, we turned on a low-level vacuum pump.

Having never tried this before, we discussed this with our patient. Being an accomplished engineer himself, he understood exactly what we trying to accomplish. He liked the idea, approved it, and we proceeded accordingly.

Daily for the next couple of weeks, we would get together on our patch-worked 'telemedicine' apparatus to examine the wound. We exchanged ideas and discussed our patient in detail each day. Gradually, the drainage decreased and finally stopped. The fever went away and the White Blood Cell count (WBC) normalized. The doctors withdrew the drain slowly, little by little every couple of days, until it was completely out and the wound healed from the inside out. We had avoided further surgical intervention, thanks to our jerry-rigged contraption. This "poor man's telemedicine" from nearly twenty-five years ago helped resolve this patient's life-threatening condition and my dilemma. My old technology experiences had come in handy.

In May 2015, the Dean of the Pharmacy and School of Health Sciences of Hebron University in Hebron, Palestine, invited me to give the keynote address for his first graduating class. It was a wonderful experience to participate in the graduation ceremony. The graduates were young people who had worked hard under very difficult living conditions. They had finally attained their academic goals and were headed on to pursue their professional careers.

At Hebron University, I felt that the faculty had made remarkable efforts to provide students with the best educational resources available to empower them to become competitive in the marketplace. However, in consideration of the geopolitical situations they were facing, I recognized it probably wasn't easy for them to invite an external guest, faculty member, or speaker on a regular basis to bring new ideas and concepts to their students.

Every university strives to cross-cultivate its educational resources with external speakers, faculty, invited guests and others. No matter how distinguished the faculty of any university is, universities strive to invite CEOs of major corporations, professors from other schools, politicians, artists, and others to their campuses. They endeavor to bring new thoughts and ideas to expose their students to alternative concepts. The more the student is exposed to, the stronger and richer the university experience becomes.

So, upon return to Atlanta, I decided that the time had come for me pursue my old telemedicine interests of the

1990s and to put them into action. By now, the technology needed had matured and had become much more affordable. It was simply a matter of determining to do what was needed, but this time I was smarter. I relied on my younger friends, students, and mentors to integrate the technology and build a website, create a syllabus, invite speakers, coordinate the educational programs and market the whole system. We invented a brand, called it the Tele Education Networks and registered it under the domain name of <u>tednets.com</u>. We then initiated a soft start by giving live, interactive seminars broadcasted and webcasted from Atlanta via a commercial internet service provider to Hebron University in Palestine.

Since then, we've added sites in multiple cities and countries. Two years later, we've given over a two dozen lectures attended by hundreds of students, doctors, nurses, technicians, and pharmacists.

On May 29, 2016, we went public at a major international event in a multi-city live transmission. Professor Arshed Quyyumi spoke on "Stem Cell Therapy in Treating Heart Disease" to an audience attending the Kurdistan Cardiac Society in Irbil – Kurdistan, Iraq. Dr. Heval Kelli, who was attending the American College of Cardiology meeting in Chicago, spoke to the same conference on "Cardiometabolic Syndrome and New Mobile Technologies in Health Care." And I spoke from Amman, Jordan on "Surgical Pulmonary Embolectomy."

It has been twenty years since my initial attempt at dabbling in telemedicine to allow tele-consultation between doctors and patients and tele-education between educators and students. It finally happened. But this time it was at a very low cost, making it incredibly more effective.

CHAPTER THIRTEEN

To Learn and to Teach
Seize the Opportunity

The best way to learn is to teach and the best way to not age is to keep working with young people. Those are two principles that I've consistently applied to my life and they have served me well.

Advancements in medicine and science are taking place at an amazingly fast pace. In order for you to keep up, you must immerse yourself in an environment that is accustomed to innovation, education, exchange of new information, and the constant sharing of knowledge. Where better than a university can you find such opportunities, particularly if your task is to train medical students, young doctors, and rising surgeons in their pursuit of careers as aspiring health care providers?

I've always enjoyed my job as a cardiac surgeon in the university environment. Teaching and learning are constants and both are a challenge and a joy. The system is built to facilitate and engender continued acquisition, building, and sharing of knowledge. There are additional side benefits that come from being an academic surgeon. In my role as such, I participate in new surgical techniques that few other surgeons have done. Because of this I've become an expert in such procedures and published papers on my work. I'm frequently invited to present at national and international conferences and travel the world over to teach other surgeons how to perform these novel procedures. My work has taken me to places that I never would have gone to on my own.

I have given lectures or performed operations in Japan, China, Indonesia, Malaysia, Singapore, Hong Kong, Turkey, France, Italy, the United Kingdom, Qatar, Dubai, Abu Dhabi, Saudi Arabia, Egypt, Tunisia, Palestine, Canada, Puerto Rico, and Mexico, and that's not the whole list! In my travels, I have seen much and made many new friends, and this wouldn't have been possible if it were not for my academic research and the university affiliation that I have maintained over the years.

As a university professor, many students and young residents have asked to spend time doing clinical rotations or research time with me. As I look back on these experiences, I think that they've been some of the most valuable encounters I've had in my career. Young people who take the time and effort to venture away from their comfort zones and travel to faraway places to explore new environments and seek new academic relations are typically very gifted and more likely to be successful. They are energetic and eager to learn and work. The ones I've had the pleasure of working with have been self-starters and are looking for other opportunities to expand their minds. Once you give them a lead, they grasp it and take off running.

In 2011, I chaired an international conference on Cardio-Metabolic Syndrome in Amman, Jordan, held at the University of Jordan College of Medicine. My guest faculty from the United States and I, along with several others from local universities and hospitals, were surprised at the number of attendees and their level of engagement in our conference. We had anticipated about a hundred attendees at the opening session, but to our surprise, over 450 participants were in the audience that day. They were attentively listening to the keynote speakers and totally engaged in this important health issue.

The entire two-and-a-half-day seminar was well attended. By the closing session, there were nearly 200 attendees still in the room to hear the last lecture. I've been to many conferences around the world and have observed that by the end of any meeting, attendee fatigue has set in and attendance is at its lowest. At our conference, to my surprise, enthusiasm still prevailed, even toward the very end of the sessions!

Later, I found out the reason our conference remained so well attended. It was because there were so many medical students in the audience. They were both enthusiastic and very motivated, as their questions were "spot-on" for the subject matter involved. They wanted to meet the faculty from the United States and to network with us, because they hoped to build bridges for future research positions, training externships, or residency slots. The students were very smart and knew what they were after. I met several of these students and was particularly impressed by two of them. These two applied and gained externships in cardiac surgery in my hospital. They spent time working with me and my colleagues, learning to work up the cardiac surgery patients and scrubbing in with me in the operating room. At the end of their rotations, they presented detailed summaries of their respective work at grand rounds. It was a great experience for them and I enjoyed working with them immensely.

The Amman conference on Cardio-Metabolic Syndrome was in fact preceded by another meeting that we had organized. It was titled "The Surgical Management of the Complex Cardiac Patient." By the time we had completed these two meetings, we realized that we had accumulated a wealth of knowledge in the presented material. So we got the idea of writing and publishing a relevant textbook based on the content of these two meetings.

Writing and publishing a medical textbook is a huge task. I've published chapters in textbooks and each chapter would take me weeks to finish. I knew that publishing an entire textbook would take much more than one person could accomplish. The idea remained in the back of my mind, but in an inactive mode.

A couple of years later, I had been invited by two of my colleagues to submit two chapters for a cardiac surgery textbook they were working on. I did so and waited to hear back on the progress of the book. To my surprise, a year after I had sent in my chapters, the publisher sent my chapters back along with a letter that had been sent to all contributors. The letter said that the publisher was withdrawing its consent to publish the book because several of the contributing authors had failed to submit their chapters, despite repeated requests. Consequently, the publisher decided it no longer wanted to complete work on the project.

There were many relevant chapters already written and ready for publishing. I seized the opportunity, contacted the two editors and offered them the opportunity to "joining forces" in merging their work with mine. We decided to publish an electronic edition; an e-book entitled "Complex Cardiac." My two colleagues and several of the other contributing authors didn't want their good work to go unused and welcomed the idea. Therefore, I rallied my team of young collaborators and researchers and invited them to get into the action.

We created the website complexcardiac.com, and invited other contributors and past speakers to busy themselves preparing their manuscripts. We then encouraged the medical students who had attended the 2011 conference at the University of Jordan to choose topics from a list we provided and to start literature searches and summarize relevant information. We then introduced "junior" contributors to the senior faculty and assigned them to write the manuscripts. The senior members were to edit the final documents.

In less than a year, our e-book came alive and is growing, with new chapters being added weekly by highly-respected authorities in cardiology, cardiac surgery, cardiac anesthesia, critical care medicine, infectious disease, pulmonary medicine, and more.

CHAPTER FOURTEEN

Anything Less than 300% Success Rate Would be an Absolute Disaster

C oming to work at my hospital is always like going on an adventure. You never know what you'll encounter that day.

I was meeting with my service chief, Dr. Robert Guyton, one morning when he got a phone call from one of our Emory cardiologists who had a specific interest in congenital cardiology. She had gotten a call about a young woman, near term with twins, having labor pains with acute pulmonary embolus (PE, a big clot in the main lung artery blocking the blood flow through the lungs and heart). To further complicate things, she also had a paradoxical embolus (also called a crossed embolism) in-transit, straddling a patent foramen ovale across the atrial septum (a clot that was about to move from the right side of the heart to the left side of the heart, risking a major stroke in the brain). Dr. Guyton said, "Well, here's Dr. Lattouf, who is our PE expert. I am sure he'll be happy to talk with you."

The young woman was immediately transferred to my hospital for further evaluation. Upon arrival, an entire team of experts assembled to examine the young mother. Showing up was the late Dr. Ken Leeper, our senior pulmonologist with a specific interest in pulmonary embolism, and a national leader in the field. He was the ultimate authority and the final decision-maker on what to do: medical therapy vs. surgical intervention. There was also a cardiologist, an intensivist, a neonatologist, a high-risk OB, an anesthesiologist—a me, the cardiac surgeon.

We had a lively discussion on what we should do. Should we proceed with medical therapy or intervene surgically? If medical, should we use anticoagulation only or should we use thrombolytic therapy?

We quickly eliminated the idea of thrombolytic therapy in a pregnant, near-term female. No one wanted to take the risk of stirring up massive uterine bleeding in a near-term pregnancy. Additionally, there was an almost paradoxical massive embolus hanging in the patent foramen ovale (PFO), straddling the inter-atrial septum that could break loose and move across into the arterial circulation and cause a fatal stroke, major cardiac event, or another catastrophic event. We discussed treating the patient with heparin alone until the babies were delivered, but we also discounted that.

The size of the saddle embolus, along with the clot in the PFO, made all of us, particularly Dr. Leeper, uneasy about waiting any further. We decided to proceed with surgical removal of the saddle embolus, extraction of the "stroke in transit," and closure of the PFO on cardiopulmonary bypass. In order to do so, we needed to first do a C-section, deliver the twin babies, and immediately proceed with the complex cardiac operation, which none of us had rehearsed or performed under these circumstances before.

I had done similar cases, but I had never done a C-Section immediately followed by cardiac surgery requiring full anticoagulation for a pulmonary embolectomy. However, I had done emergency valve surgeries after C-sections for women with critical mitral stenosis who had presented in severe congestive heart failure at time of delivery.

We each knew our responsibilities and set about to fulfill them. We were starting with one critically ill patient and planned to end with three reasonably healthy beings. We had to have a 300% success rate, not 200% and certainly not 100%. Anything less than a 300% success rate would be a complete failure. We all knew it and our thoughts about the risks lead to some tense moments.

The preparations began. One operating room was prepared for the mom's C-section, to be immediately followed by a complex open-heart procedure. The adjacent operating room was converted into a high-risk neonatal ICU.

A team of doctors and nurses from the neonatal unit descended with incubators, instruments, miniature needles, stethoscopes, bronchoscopes, intravenous lines, bags, tubes, and linens. They quickly converted my usual operating room into a neonatal recovery room for the two newborns.

After the room was ready, the senior neonatologist gave the signal to the attending, high-risk OB to proceed with the C-Section. The mom was already on the operating room table, but was still awake. She had been prepped and draped from her neck to her ankles, with double draping from the mid-abdomen and above, to keep the sternum and chest separate from the lower abdominal and pelvic area. The extra draping was in case my team and I had to move in promptly and place the patient on cardiopulmonary bypass due to hemodynamic deterioration.

Time was of the essence—the clot might move at any time.

A C-section followed by complex cardiac surgeries requires general anesthesia. General anesthesia requires medications that would cross into the placenta and affect the babies' level of consciousness, depress their ability to breath, and slow their heart rate, putting their lives at risk.

Accordingly, when a pregnant mom is given general anesthesia, it becomes a race against time, and the high-risk OB doctors must make incisions in the lower abdomen, open the uterus, and deliver the baby as quickly and safely as possible. They must watch the cardiac monitors closely to avoid the circulating medication from reducing the heart rate and respiration, causing permanent damage to the child.

Our two high-risk OB surgeons scrubbed in and were ready to make the incision. My assistant and I scrubbed-in and stood by, ready to go. My scrub nurse, the OB scrub nurse, and other support staff members were ready with all their equipment on standby. My perfusionist was ready with the heart-lung machine, equipment and lines primed and connected to the operating room table. The anesthesiologist had her drugs in hand; ready to push into the patient's veins and quickly put her to sleep. An endotracheal tube was nearby, ready to place into her trachea and start ventilation with highly concentrated oxygen and other anesthetic agents.

Once the anesthesiologist said, "patient asleep," the OB docs wasted no time and made an incision in the patient's lower abdomen. With uterus in hand, one doctor carefully made another incision to reveal the twins and began pulling the babies out and handing them to a nurse, who ran next door to the improvised neonatal ICU. And as fast as the two babies were delivered, the two doctors took large sutures and quickly closed the uterus.

Another suture line and the various layers of the abdominal wall were closed. They were done in less than fifteen minutes, from incision to closure. I was stunned at the speed and efficiency of their actions.

The OB doctors moved out and we placed another set of drapes over their work area. The previously prepped and draped chest area was untouched and remained sterile. My team and I moved ahead with our part of the procedure.

I performed the usual sternotomy, gave the heparin, and placed the patient on total cardiopulmonary bypass. I then placed a vent in the ascending aorta to remove any air bubble from the aorta. I removed the clot in transit, closed the PFO, opened the pulmonary arteries and removed the large clots from them. I then did de-airing maneuvers, took her off the heart-lung, and closed the chest.

We went into the operating room with one live patient and came out with three live ones. Anything less than a 300% success rate would have been indeed an absolute disaster!

CHAPTER FIFTEEN

From a Dishwasher to a Doctor
The Value of Mentorship

About twelve years ago, while my daughter Amal was in her early high school years at Pace Academy, she came to me one day and asked, "Dad, my friend Moe asked me if his brother Heval could ask you some questions about how to apply to medical school. He desperately wants to go, but has no one to guide him through the process!"

I said, "Tell me more about Moe and Heval." Amal continued, "Moe is captain of our soccer team at Pace and is a really good player. He has won many games for our school and he's a good student, too. He and his family are refugees from Syria and newcomers to the Atlanta area. I said, "Sure, feel free to pass my cell number to Moe and he can give it to his brother. I'd be more than happy to speak with him."

A few days later, I got a call from Heval, who seemed somewhat shy, reserved, and hesitant in asking for help or guidance. I invited him over to our home one Saturday morning for coffee and he arrived right on time.

He had quite an intriguing story to tell and I listened intently. He shared the painful details of his family's relocation from Syria through Germany to his new residence in the United States. Initially, his mom, dad, and younger brother Moe had lived as political refugees in Germany where Heval was began his eleventh-grade year of high school. His first barrier to continuing his education was that he didn't speak a word of German or English. Going to school in Germany wasn't particularly welcoming experience, nor was it fun, he recalled. Gang fights were common and it was a constant challenge to survive the cultural clashes between the many different ethnic groups.

One day, as a friend of his Heval and Moe's father was applying for immigration to the United States, he encouraged the father to apply for an immigration visa, too. The funny thing about this was his father hadn't even considered it. Heval and his father decided to accept the recommendation and submitted an application for immigration as a refugee to the American embassy.

To their surprise, they received a call from the US Consulate in Germany, were interviewed, and soon thereafter received approval for their immigration to the States. Their good fortune brought them to Atlanta, where unfortunately they knew no one.

After exhausting the initial support that our federal government provides new refugees, they had to find ways to support themselves. By then, Heval was starting his senior year in high school, while his younger brother was beginning his freshman year. To make ends meet, Heval found a dishwashing job at a local Mediterranean restaurant in Decatur. He was paid only minimum wage, but it was enough to support himself and his family. Nine months later, he graduated from high school and was accepted into the pre-med track at Georgia State University.

Heval told me, "I knew that my education was the only way out of poverty and I had to work hard to survive, succeed and excel." He then made a statement that I will never forget. He said, "I promised myself that for every dish I washed at the restaurant each day, I would go home and read a page in a book each night. By doing so, I became an avid reader and taught myself English."

I was amazed by the dedication and commitment this young man had shown. I was also impressed by his determination to be successful through education. I couldn't imagine how someone who had arrived in this country only a year earlier had learned the difficult language of English in such a short time. He had graduated from high school, got accepted into college and was about to graduate with straight A's. He had proven his commitment by mastering the extremely difficult, pre-med curriculum at a major university.

We spent a couple more hours chatting when I told him, "If you can survive the refugee camps of Germany, teach yourself English a year after arriving in this country, graduate from high school and Georgia State University with excellent grades, I see no reason why you shouldn't be able to make it into medical school." I went further and said, "All you need is someone to encourage you and show you the path ahead. Believe me, you will be successful."

I invited Heval to stay in touch and to let me know when he was applying to medical school. Months later, he called and returned to our home for another visit. It was time to submit applications to medical schools and he asked me for a letter of recommendation. I wrote him one and actually did a little more. I called a colleague of mine who was a cardiologist and on the admissions committee of a medical school and made a strong recommendation on Heval's behalf.

Heval was granted an interview and he was accepted. Medical school isn't easy, but I am sure he worked very hard to make the high grades that he did. He seemed to enjoy it and thrive under a high-level, intense workload. Four years later, he graduated at the top of his class and was accepted and completed an internal medicine residency in one of the most competitive programs in the country. Currently, he's on his way to completing his fellowship in cardiology in one of the top cardiology training centers in the world.

During his internal medicine residency, Heval stopped by my house one day for a visit. In his usual timid and shy manner, he asked if I was involved in any research projects that he could help me with. It seemed to me that research was Heval's ultimate form of entertainment, or so he made it sound. It just so happened that I was interested in a new project and was researching the influence of cardiometabolic syndrome (CMS) on the long-term survival of the patients who had undergone coronary artery bypass operations. Cardiometabolic syndrome is a collection of diseases that includes diabetes, high blood pressure, obesity and elevated blood lipids. When two or more of these are present in an individual, the risk for development of diseases of the heart, kidneys, and brain dramatically increase. In my long experience in heart surgery, I developed an impression that patients who had CMS didn't do as well with recovery as patients who didn't have it. Consequently, I wanted to review the literature and find support for my hypothesis.

I had pulled dozens of referenced articles and started to read them when Heval came to visit. He offered to help with my literature review and I gladly accepted his offer. I gave him copies of my references and journal articles and asked him to come back with some thoughts once his reviews were completed. He said, "Give me a few weeks and I'll be back with a summary for your review."

Six weeks later, Heval e-mailed me a sixty-page document summarizing the most important articles in the medical literature on CMS. He had summarized 157 articles. It was an amazing accomplishment in such a short period of time. How he had found the time to do this side project when, as an internal medicine resident, he was already busy with several other research projects and numerous clinical responsibilities?

To say that I was immensely impressed by Heval's work would be an understatement. In my eyes, he was no longer just a student or resident, but was my research colleague and collaborator. After this, we published several manuscripts together and held many international seminars and summits jointly in the United States and around the world. We initiated a series of business and research activities that involved not only the two of us, but also the Department of Public Health for the State of Georgia and collaborations in Canada, China, India, Dubai, England, Jordan, Kurdistan and several other countries. Heval became an internationally recognized authority on cardiometabolic syndrome.

I learned from working with Heval, that mentorship is a two-way street. Just as I had mentored Heval in his early days in college when he didn't know how to apply to medical school, I learned that the same process could be just as valuable for my family members and me.

When my daughter Amal graduated from college and was undecided whether to apply to medical school or dental school, I called several of my dentist friends and asked them if she could shadow them. They were most kind and several agreed to allow her to. She loved what she observed and quickly realized that dentistry was closer than medicine to what she wanted in a career. She liked the science, but loved the hand-eye coordination and the fine and focused work even more. She completed her dental school studies and since then, has been doing her residency training and excelling at a remarkable level. My dentist friends' work with Amal paralleled my work with Heval, I had mentored Heval and my dentist colleagues had mentored my daughter Amal. They both had exceeded their mentors' expectations, too.

These two experiences led Heval and me to push the envelope even further. We both decided that if, in our small world, our mentorships had created such positive results and led to great new friendships, we could duplicate the process on the national international stage. Our goals were to expand our sphere of influence and create a more formal mentorship program. We could develop new research, share publications, promote international collaboration, and much more.

Four years ago, Heval and I took the bold step; we invited several community leaders to a meeting and launched a new, non-profit organization called Mentorship Atlanta (MA). Since then, MA has held four annual mentorship conferences with national speakers that included the current president of the American University of Beirut; the past president of Delta Airline's technical operations responsible for the safety of all Delta airplanes; the president of Home Depot; the president of Coca Cola; Professor Jag Sheth, the internationally respected marketing guru; Dr. Erika James, Dean of the Emory Business School; and many more distinguished national and international speakers.

All this happened because my teenage daughter asked me if I would meet Moe's brother Heval to advise him on how to apply to medical school. It didn't occur to me then that when I said "yes" to her request, that it would lead to an entire journey that has influenced the lives of many hundreds of people, mine included, in a very powerful and wonderful way.

Thank you, Amal, for making that request twelve or so years ago. And thank you Heval, Moe, and all the people who have contributed to the great work that has made the work of Cardiometabolic Research and Mentorship Atlanta possible.

NOTE: Mentorship Atlanta has since been renamed U-Beyond and is registered with the State of Georgia as a non-profit, 501(c)3 Organization.

CHAPTER SIXTEEN

How I Became Interested in Lung Clots
At a Moment's Notice

I came home Friday, March 18, 2016, after having dinner with my wife at a neighborhood Japanese restaurant, and I was looking forward to a quiet evening. Since I was on call for my hospital system, I didn't expect the quiet to last long. Sure enough, I received an interesting text message from a cardiology colleague at Emory University Hospital. He'd heard that I had developed a notable reputation for managing acute pulmonary embolism and providing surgical care for these critically ill patients who otherwise wouldn't survive.

It was very kind of him to send me such a flattering note. As I began to draft a reply, it occurred to me how I became interested in this disease entity and I shared it in my reply to him. I had always known the reasons behind my special interest in this cruel disease state that reportedly kills between 150,000-200,000 Americans each year, but I had never talked much about it. That night, something inside me pushed me to discuss it for the first time.

My interest in fatal pulmonary embolism goes back nearly a quarter of a century, when a dear friend lost his 22-year-old daughter, Mona, one year after she had gotten married and a couple of days after she'd delivered her one and only son. Oddly enough, the child's name was Omar. My friend, Farouk, was devastated over the sudden loss of his daughter and who wouldn't be?

The sequence of tragic events went something like this: Mona had just given birth two days earlier to a beautiful son. When she got out of bed one morning and appeared to have fainted. As she hit the floor, she immediately began turning blue as her heart quit beating. She was rushed to a nearby hospital where she was declared dead on arrival.

On autopsy, a large clot was found in the main pulmonary artery as it exited the right ventricle to the lungs. This caused a total blockage of the main pulmonary artery and prevented blood from flowing into the lungs, into the left heart, and on to the rest of the body.

Under normal circumstances blood flows through the right heart into the pulmonary artery, then into the lungs where it's oxygenated to it rid of carbon dioxide. It then returns to the left heart and gets pumped out to every organ of the body.

When blood fails to flow through the heart and lungs, the brain and other vital organs cannot survive for long. In particular, the brain is very sensitive to the loss of blood supply. It only takes three minutes of lost blood flow before irreversible brain damage occurs. In medical terms, this right heart outflow obstruction is called massive pulmonary embolism (PE). As I went through medical school and residency, Mona's story never left my mind.

Pulmonary emboli are caused by blood clotting in the large veins of the legs and pelvis, usually in patients who have been in sedentary conditions and/or have hypercoagulability medical issues. Postpartum women are particularly at increased risk of developing deep vein thrombosis and accordingly, are at risk of death. Since that day, I've made it a habit, when I've traveled to Amman to stop in and visit a few hours with Farouk and his family. Farouk and his wife practically raised their grandson in their home and showered him with love and affection.

Every time I visited Farouk, he would talk about his beloved daughter, whom he greatly missed. Until the day he died, Farouk never let Mona go. He kept her memory alive and present in his daily life; always bringing tears to his eyes regardless of how many years had passed.

Memories have been embedded in my mind, too—about Farouk, his grandson Omar, and the untimely death of the young mother who had everything to live for. They all became part of my world of pulmonary emboli. Saddle pulmonary embolism was no longer just another cardiovascular killer disease that killed hundreds of thousands of people worldwide; it had become personal. After all, it was the condition that orphaned young Omar two days after his birth and forever made my friend Farouk, a sad and broken-hearted dad.

Pulmonary embolism became a personal challenge for me. As I continued my early career in cardiac surgery, PE became one of those conditions that I was determined to conquer each and every time I encountered it. You might call it a personal vendetta against an enemy that had caused dear friends of mine great pain and anguish.

I studied pulmonary embolism intensely and read the history behind it. I read every medical article I could get my hands on. In doing so, I came to realize that the methods of treatment for PE hadn't improved over the years. However, considerable scientific advances in other cardiovascular diseases were moving forward at a rapid pace. For instance, significant technological advances in treating myocardial infarctions and strokes of the brain had dramatically improved outcomes.

But treatments for PE had been stagnant for years and consisted of mostly giving blood thinners in the form of heparin to thin the blood to prevent more clots from forming. All you can do then is to wait and see if the clot shrinks. Or you use a clot-buster such as streptokinase (STK) to accelerate dissolution of the clot. The problem with these two approaches is that they haven't been proven to have very successful outcomes. In fact, for patients with a symptomatic large clot load, the 90-day death rates after receiving treatment with either of the above meds approaches 50%.

Old data on surgical treatment didn't have good outcomes either. However, when you review those patients who were operated on, you find that they had their surgeries much too late in the course of their illnesses. In fact, more recent data indicate that early intervention in the management of pulmonary embolism results in much more encouraging news, with operative survival rates of critically ill patients approaching 94%.

Encouraged by the later data, I decided to take a more aggressive approach in managing these very sick and unstable PE patients. I was lucky in that one of my medical colleagues at my hospital, Dr. Ken Leeper, was an international authority in the field and was a believer in an early surgical approach for these patients. Having done few surgical embolectomies before, I told him that I was readily available to serve his patients' needs anytime.

Ken advocated early surgical intervention for massive and certain sub-massive PEs. Massive PEs are defined as clots lodged in pulmonary arteries that have caused a drop in blood pressure, for 15 minutes or more, below 90 mm Hg. Or the clots may be causing symptoms, such as heart block. Sub-massive PEs are clots that show poor function in the right heart, evidence of heart attack. Or the size of the right heart approaches the size of the left heart.

Together, we assembled several dozen cases of successful operative procedures without a single operative death. We followed these patients, some up to ten years, and demonstrated no heart or recurrent PE-related deaths.

Our record was one of the best in the country. Dr. Leeper had a great understanding of the pathophysiology of pulmonary circulation and would make the call on whom to operate on and on whom to use medical therapy only. His judgment was unparalleled. I had the technical skills and determination to keep patients alive during and after my surgeries and he continued to select the appropriate patients. And to our good fortune, we both had great anesthesia and critical care teams who provided superior services around the clock. Our teams were able to tackle some of the most difficult cases and salvage patients who otherwise wouldn't have survived.

My interest and improved skills in managing patients with massive PEs came in handy five years ago, when a young woman with massive PE was referred to me from a local hospital. She was in her 28th week of pregnancy with twins. I shared this heart-warming story with you in an earlier chapter.

Dr. Ken Leeper was a great friend, distinguished educator, and beloved colleague. Everyone who met him fell in love with Ken. In 2015, Ken was a patient himself and had a surgical procedure. A few days after, he died suddenly at home. We suspected that the cause of death might have been a massive pulmonary embolus, but didn't know for sure.

The practice of medicine lost a great leader with the untimely departure of Ken. He taught so many people that the best medicine was practiced with a heavy dose of compassion.

In your memory Ken, and in the memories of Farouk and Mona, I dedicate this chapter.

May you all rest in peace.

CHAPTER SEVENTEEN

The Man, the Operation, and the Love Story

O n Tuesday morning, March 15, 2016, I was getting into my car to head to the hospital for another day of patient-care rounds and cardiac surgeries, thinking about a complex, thoracic abdominal aneurysm from the previous day, when my iPhone signaled an incoming message.

I hadn't even turned over the ignition yet. I paused, lifted my phone and checked the email message. I was from someone named "Mitch."

The name wasn't a common one, and I could only recall one person in my past with that name. Could it be him? The email went something like this:

> "Dr. Lattouf, I hope you haven't forgotten me... I'll never forget you! I am doing great! I retired last May at 68 and didn't know if I would ever see that day. I thank God for you, and that He put you in my life, so that I may spend several more years loving, and being loved, by my beautiful wife, Rose!! Thank you again. You are a Good Man!! I love You♥ Mitchell"

My mind began scanning my memory banks trying to recall an encounter with Mitchell. Like a fast-running movie, the memory of our prior meeting quickly came to mind.

It began with a phone call from Dr. John Attokaren, a cardiologist colleague, about five years ago. In his usual tone of voice he said, "Omar, I have a difficult situation that I need your help on. A very nice, otherwise healthy, patient of mine needs a redo. Specifically, he requires a coronary artery bypass and mitral valve replacement. He does, however, have a prior functioning mechanical aortic valve in place." Have I mentioned more than a dozen times how much I dislike redoing cardiac surgeries?

"Well, it will be challenging, but it's doable," I said. Then John went on: "The big problem is that he received Cobalt radiation 39 years ago for mediastinal lymphoma, and now his aorta is very badly calcified. He's been turned down by other surgeons, and was told it's inoperable."

I told Dr. Attokaren that the case sounded very difficult, and it could well be inoperable based on the information he had provided. But John didn't stop there. He asked me to please see his patient in consultation before making my decision. He repeated, "This patient is really a very nice man and I'd like for you to meet him."

Dr. Attokaren had always been a straight shooter with me, and I had learned to trust his judgment. He had previously referred difficult cases to me, but he'd always prepared those cases well. He always gave me a "heads-up" in advance and luckily our common patients had always done well.

Accompanied by his wife, the patient showed up at my office a couple of weeks later: a tall, very handsome, Italian-looking gentleman with his very sharp and well-dressed spouse.

As we went through his detailed history and physical examination, I learned that Mitch was on his second career. He drove a school bus and it proved to be a labor of love.

Every morning and afternoon, he picked up and delivered children from their homes to their school and back. He loved what he did and he was loved by "his" school children.

His chest pain and shortness of breath were starting to concern him and he was afraid he would have a heart attack while driving the bus and risk the lives of those precious school children. His symptoms of pain and difficulty breathing were getting worse to the point that he was unable to carry on with his daily activities and felt that something had to be done soon.

As he and his wife sat there in my exam room reciting their story, I saw that their wish was to move forward with a healthier life. I was watching his wife Rose's face, and although she rarely spoke, her expression spoke volumes. She was hanging onto every word Mitch said, and was waiting to hear what I would recommend.

We reviewed his heart cath together and it was obvious that he had severe disease. The heavily-calcified left main arterial stenosis couldn't be ignored. Dr. Attokaren hadn't exaggerated the extent and severity of the calcification.

I shared my concern with the family that surgery would be very challenging, but I needed more information. I ordered a CT scan of his chest to assess the degree of aortic calcification and asked them to come back again once I had the results. In a way, I gave myself a bit of breathing room to reflect on the case.

Mitch and Rose returned a couple of weeks later with the CT scan results, and indeed, the aorta was an "egg shell" of calcification. While a normal aorta is less than 2 mm thick with no calcium on it, his anterior aorta was almost one centimeter thick and totally calcified. Mitch's aorta was undeniably, untouchable. There was no way to cannulate the ascending aorta (inserting a tube in order to go on the heart lung machine), apply a clamp, or place grafts to it—all steps of the usual coronary artery bypass.

During our second visit, I shared with Mitch and Rose my concerns. They listened intently. The more I talked, the more Rose held tightly onto Mitch's arm, as if she didn't want to let him go. At that moment, I stopped being a heart surgeon, and became a witness to an amazing love story between a woman who loved her man, holding tightly onto him as if she were afraid I was about to be take him away from her.

The sight of her holding so tightly onto his arm without saying a single word took me back to my early college years and one of my all-time, favorite movies, *Love Story*. I had seen this film no less than a dozen times and listened to its theme song dozens more. As Mitch and Rose sat in my office, they took me back to the early 1970s and reminded me of the romantic scenes between the two young lovers—the Harvard University law student Oliver Barrett (Ryan O'Neal) and his dream girl Jenny Cavilleri (Ali McGraw).

In those moments I became interested in my two new friends, Rose and Mitch, their school bus, the school children, the affection they felt for those children, and their love for one another.

I was frank and transparent, telling them that the surgery would be high-risk and he might not survive. They both looked me in the face and said with no hesitation, "We understand, but we want you to do it." Knowing that it was going to exhaust me both physically and emotionally, I scheduled the operation. While I had successfully done this type of surgery many times before, this time it was different. I was emotionally connected in a deeper way than ever before.

On the morning of surgery, I planned the course of the operation in detail. I rehearsed every step of the procedure in advance of making the first incision. I wasn't willing to add any more risks to the procedure. I asked my most senior physician assistants to help pull the radial artery and harvest the veins. I couldn't use the internal mammary artery, because it was very likely damaged by the heavy-dose radiation, just like the aorta and the left main were.

To open the chest safely, I exposed and cannulated the right axillary artery and right femoral vein, and went on bypass before opening the breastbone to decompress the heart and reduce the risk of major bleeding.

Once he was on bypass and the chest fully open, I palpated the aorta and indeed it was like a steel pipe with no place for clamps, stitches, grafting or anything whatsoever. It was a "no touch zone." I needed to examine the mitral valve and evaluate if the stenosis that was shown in the pre-operative echocardiogram was indeed as severe as stated. The intra-operative echo showed poor mobility of the anterior leaflet, but the gradient across the valve wasn't very high—good! The relative low gradient was comforting, thus I called my in-house cardiologist and Dr. Attokaren to share my new findings.

They both insisted that I physically examine the mitral valve to make a definitive assessment. So, on a beating heart, I opened the left atrium and examined the mitral valve. The posterior leaflet was pliable and freely moving. The anterior leaflet was like a piece of glass fixed in one position, thickened and immobile. The anterior leaflet was one continuous piece of solid rock, attached in continuity with the aorta. I quickly realized that taking out the anterior leaflet of the mitral valve would put me in contact with a sheet of solid rock that I couldn't drive my needles through.

I decided to back out of the left atrium, closed its wall, and focused my attention on bypassing the coronary arteries. I performed three grafts on the arteries and went up to the artery that supplies blood to the right side of the brain, the innominate artery. I applied a partial clamp to it, and connected my grafts to its side; a trick I had devised some 20 years earlier when confronted with a similar but less intense situation.

The outcome? With the aid of an intra-aortic balloon pump, nitric oxide, and several days on the ventilator in the ICU, Mitch made complete recovery. He was fully functional when discharged and later returned to the clinic for follow-up. He looked to be in great shape and had returned to the job he loved so dearly. From time to time I would hear that he was doing well.

When I received Mitch's lovely message, it truly touched my heart. I returned the favor by emailing the following:

> Mitch and Rose,
> Thank you for the note.
> You made my day.
> I love you, too. ♥

CHAPTER EIGHTEEN

Saving Nicolas

When my son Rashid was barely two years old, he would tell his mom, "When I grow up, I don't want to be a doctor, because Daddy misses cartoons in both the morning and the evening." At that time, 1988, I was a chief resident in cardiothoracic surgery at Emory University, which has one of the busiest and most demanding programs in the country.

I certainly did miss the "morning cartoons," because my days started with making ICU rounds at 6:30 am and wouldn't end until 9:00 or 10:00 pm in the evening. I missed the "evening cartoons," too—hardly acceptable to Rashid. He never changed his mind and wanted nothing to do with the practice of medicine.

Years later, on a summer Sunday afternoon, Rashid and his friend Nicolas were going out to lunch and to look at cars. Both were excited, as they were about to enter their senior year in college. Rashid was attending Emory University and Nicolas was at Stetson University. They invited me to join them and I gladly accepted. Rashid introduced me to Nick at a local restaurant where we had lunch, and off we went to test drive Porsches. I had never driven one, so I thought it would be fun and decided to accompany them to the dealership.

We went to a dealer in Buckhead district of Atlanta, and asked him to allow us to take a test-drive one. The dealer wouldn't let us drive the car, but did allow us to ride with a driver who took us on a thrilling ride through the streets of Buckhead. It was an impressive car, and we did have a fun afternoon. There were no tough negotiations or purchases were made. We were done, so we left for our respective homes.

That was my first time meeting Nick and spending some time with him, although Rashid spoke a lot about him. They were very close friends in high school and in college, even though they attended different schools. Nick and Rashid had a lot in common: both were born in Atlanta, came from immigrant parents, had "brown skin," and shared an interest in the same field of study—business, capital markets, and finance.

Some months later, I received a tense and disturbing phone call from Rashid. He asked, "Dad, do you remember my friend Nick, the one we went with to test drive Porsches one Sunday afternoon?" I said, "Sure, I remember Nick. How could I forget him, since you both look so much alike that you could be mistaken for brothers?" Rashid said, "Nick's mom just called and told me that Nick was involved in an accident while riding his motorcycle in Los Angeles. He was hit by a truck and has very severe head and bodily injuries. He's currently is in coma, and the doctors don't know if he'll survive."

As Rashid was telling me the bad news, I felt a cold rush come over my body, while imagining what the injury was like, and what was happening to Nick. As I gathered more information, I learned that Nick was riding his motorcycle in Hollywood when a truck ran a red light, knocking him off his bike and landing him on the street, unconscious. An

146

ambulance took him to Cedars-Sinai Medical Center in West Hollywood, where emergency care was instituted. It wasn't until the following morning that the hospital was able to connect with his parents in Atlanta and notify them of his condition.

Once Nick's dad received the news, he immediately flew from New York to see him and ended up staying there for quite some time. Rashid asked me to inquire from the doctors about Nick's prognosis. He wanted to know if it was as bad as he had heard, and if they were going to make him a "No Code" ("Do Not Resuscitate" or "allow natural death").

I called Neeraj, Nick's dad, who was already at the hospital, and spoke with him at great length. Neeraj was devastated, and quite lachrymose, over his son's injuries. He told me that Nick was on a respirator, not responsive, and had a severe head injury documented by the CT scan. There were twenty-six bleeding sites in the brain, and the doctors had put a device in Nick's skull to monitor his intracranial pressure.

Nick's injuries were almost too numerous to mention. He had a cervical spine injury, fractured ribs that caused lung contusion and required chest tube insertion, and a crush injury to the thoracic spinal cord that would leave him paralyzed from the chest down, should he survive. In addition, he had other fractures in his arms and legs that would require further surgical intervention.

The doctors weren't hopeful that Nick would survive, what with the numerous and complex injuries to his body. They had indeed mentioned to Neeraj a "No Code Status" or "Do Not Resuscitate-DNR" order, which meant that no heroic measures would be taken if he were to quit breathing. Hearing that, I asked Neeraj to do a clinical test for me. I instructed, "Go get a flash light and open Nick's eyes, shine the light in one eye. Tell me what happens to the pupil in that eye and the pupil in the other eye."

This is a test called a "pupillary reflex test," commonly used by neurologists and neurosurgeons to assess midbrain function in patients who have sustained some level of brain injury. If the pupils fail to respond to light, it usually means that there has been severe midbrain damage and survival is very unlikely. If both pupils react to light when it's shined into one eye, then the brain damage is likely limited, and chances of survival are high, particularly in a young person in his twenties. In some cases, the interpretation of the test is limited if a patient has received certain drugs that act directly on the pupillary muscle fibers.

Neeraj called me back and said, "Both pupils reacted and constricted when light was shined into one eye". Hearing that, I assured him that the brain damage was not irreversible and Nick's chances of survival were not small at all. Thus, I told Neeraj not to sign the DNR documents and to insist on "Full Code" status, which meant that if Nick's heart were to stop suddenly for any reason, the nurses and doctors would do everything possible to get his heart to beat again.

In my experience, once you place a DNR code status on a patient, it's like admitting, "It's OK if this patient dies." Thus, I never allow it to be used unless everyone understands that all efforts have been made and failed, there is absolutely no chance whatsoever for survival, *and* the entire family agrees to the critical decision.

In Nick's case, I was convinced that he was salvageable, and accordingly, I conveyed that to his Dad, who held to that decision with all his might. From then on, the plan was clear: we were going to do everything possible to save Nick we weren't going to listen to any more suggestions of DNR.

Rashid and his friend Mark wanted to fly to Los Angeles the following weekend to see Nick and asked me to join them, which I did. We flew from Atlanta to LA on Saturday morning and went directly to see him in the Cedars ICU.

Upon our arrival, Neeraj immediately took us in to see Nick. He was on the ventilator, supported by numerous machines with arterial and venous lines, chest tubes, an intracranial monitor, and many other devices connected to him. Nick was comatose and non-responsive, except for his pupils being reactive to bright light. Rashid, Mark, and I spent Saturday and Sunday with Nick and Neeraj. We flew back to Atlanta on Sunday afternoon.

Over the following three months, we all stayed in touch and received regular reports from Neeraj on Nick's progress. I served as the "back door" family doctor, advising Nick's parents on interpretation of various studies, tests, and reports. Gradually, Nick started to open his eyes and to make small movements with his fingers, but not his legs or feet. The CT scans had shown a crushing injury to the mid-spinal cord region, leaving no doubt that there would be severe neurological damage to both legs, as well as bladder and bowel control functions.

As weeks went by, Nick's condition stabilized. He was being fed through a tube placed through the abdominal wall and inserted directly into the stomach, called a PEG feeding tube. He was breathing through a tracheostomy, a plastic pipe inserted through a cut in the neck and going directly into the windpipe. When Nick became stable enough that he could be moved back to Atlanta, where his family lived, I arranged for him to be admitted to a special unit in my hospital that provided the required, specialized care.

Due to his ongoing immobility, Nick was unable to fly in a regular plane seat; he needed a special medical evacuation plane to fly him safely home. Luckily, his employer and its insurance company agreed to foot the bill for the expensive medevac flight from Los Angeles to Atlanta. Nick came back to his home town and was admitted directly into my hospital. My colleagues—intensivists and pulmonary medicine doctors—cared for Nick, and as usual, provided excellent care.

Slowly, Nick made further recovery and began to fully open his eyes and grasp with his hands. He was still unable to sit, speak, eat, or drink on his own. After several weeks in my hospital, Nick was weaned off the ventilator and the tracheostomy tube was removed. Now, he finally could breathe on his own and began to take food by mouth, which was leading to being weaned off the feeding tube.

At that stage, the need for physical rehabilitation was the next limiting step to Nick's recovery. We needed to get him into one of the world's best rehab centers, the Shepherd Spinal Center, which luckily was located right up the road on Peachtree Street in Atlanta. I had operated there in the past; I knew the doctors and administrators, which might make things a little easier. So I made a few phone calls to some of my friends at Shepherd and Nick was placed on the waiting list. Shortly afterwards, he was transferred to this world-class institution.

Shepherd is an amazing place, a great hospital totally dedicated to the care and recovery of people injured in accidents and suffering from sustained, severe neurological trauma. Without such specialized care, chances of survival or meaningful recovery would be in serious question. My prior experiences with Shepherd were awesome. Every patient who went there made a good recovery. So, when Nick was accepted at Shepard, I felt that we were given a vote of confidence that he'd make a good recovery, too.

On a stretcher and via ambulance, Nick made it to Shepard and the hard road to recovery began. Nick was taught to become mobile using a wheelchair, get in and out of bed into his chair, feed himself, dress himself and perform many body functions that we take for granted. Shepard worked with Nick on speech therapy and mental function as well as physical exercises. While he was totally dependent upon others on admission, he was now becoming more independent every day.

A year later, Nick was in much better shape and was to face another big challenge. On his birthday, his friends decided to buy him an iPad, so they could communicate with him by email and Skype. This was a brilliant idea as it gave Nick something to look forward to and a mechanism to reconnect him with his peers. Emails started flowing back and forth between Nick and his friends. Sometimes, Nick or Rashid would copy me on emails addressing his continued progress.

We all began reflecting on how he could get professionally engaged again. We knew that Nick had become an analyst for Morgan Stanley (as were the majority of his friends), so it was natural to consider something that would get him involved in his field again. I called Nick and suggested that he would do a blog on the stock market and write an article twice a month. He could analyze the market and make predictions of likely movements. This was to be based on what other experts in the field thought.

With help from other friends, the blog was created and Nick began writing and posting his articles on the financial markets. He wrote many posts that I enjoyed reading, and I learned a lot from him. I found out later that Nick enjoyed researching and writing them, too.

He continued to make substantial progress, both physically and mentally. As we continued to communicate, I found find his articles to be of high quality—much higher than anything I could have written myself. His choice of vocabulary, grammar, sentence structure, and delivery of concepts were impressive. People who have read them can't believe that a person who had severe brain injury, and was almost a "DNR and No Code," wrote those articles!

In our meetings, I would encourage Nick to consider re-engaging in a career that wouldn't require him to travel, something that he could do from a home office. He decided that he would go to graduate school and started to prepare for the Graduate Record Exam. I knew he was studying hard for the test when his "market analysis" blog dried up.

Then, on May 24, 2016, I got an email from Nick saying, "I earnestly believe that preparing for each essay, using dense knowledge and varied vocabulary, and writing the Market Analysis, REALLY helped me perform well on the GRE. I scored an unimpressive, 65th percentile on the quantitative portion, but an awesome 90th percentile on the verbal portion. I COMPLETELY attribute performing so incredibly well on this portion of the test to writing essays for you. It really caused me to unconsciously prepare. So clearly, your rather un-medical request is proving EVERYTHING the world-leading neurologists at Cedars-Sinai said to be mostly INCORRECT. You've really given me one of the greatest gifts imaginable."

That was an awesome email. It made my day, brought tears to my eyes, and made my heart skip a beat. How could a young man be so kind to give me such undeserved praise, when I was simply doing my job as a physician and helping my son's best friend?

I wrote Nick back:

"CONGRATULATIONS.

That is awesome.

I am so happy for you.

That said, you are correct on one count and wrong on another. You are right that you have proved the Cedars-Sinai docs wrong with your very impressive recovery and success!

You are wrong that I deserve any credit for your hard work. I was simply cheering you on while you were doing all the hard work.

But, I'll gladly accept the compliment.

GO NICK.............

I believed you could do it all along, and never doubted you for a minute.

I'm so happy for you.

Omar"

From Left to Right: Rashid L, Ravi N, Mark S., Nicolas U.

CHAPTER NINETEEN

Goodbye, My Little Friend

Goodbye Samir

W hen she was three years old, my daughter Amal would repeatedly tell me, "When I grow up, I want to be a doctor so that you can work with me."

In May of 2015, Amal graduated from Boston University's dental school and moved to Texas for further training. As a resident at the prestigious University of Texas Post-Graduate Dental Residency Program, one of her tasks was to interview applicants for the General Dentistry Practice Residency. A question she asked one applicant led to a series of unexpected events. That question and the answer became the prelude to a life-changing experience for many people— including me!

The simple question she asked was, "What was one of the most exciting things you did recently?" Without hesitation, the applicant answered, "Volunteering at Al-Zaatari Syrian Refugee Camp in Northern Jordan!"

Amal isn't a person to keep track of international political events and she knew nothing about the Zaatari camp. However, she did know a little about the ongoing Syrian crisis and the massive refugee problem resulting from the instability in that region. She called me and I briefed her on what had been happening.

I thought that was the end of the story. I figured that she would go back to her usual areas of interest: dental training, exercise, planning her future practice, and the other things that young people in the USA are concerned about.

A few weeks later, Amal called again. This time she said, "I want to volunteer at Al-Zaatari and have already called SAMS (Syrian American Medical Society). They have a mission trip going in January 2016 and I want to volunteer. Will you go with me?" Without a second thought, I said "Yes, of course."

In the back of my mind, I recalled what she had told me twenty-four years earlier. While she wouldn't be going as a practicing physician, she would be fulfilling her "promise" to work with me in a field just as important to these refugees.

Word gets around quickly in our family and the next thing I heard from my youngest daughter Zeena was that she'd decided to go with us. Zeena, a senior in college at Emory University, decided that she would do her senior thesis on "Women's and Children's Aspirations for Education at Al-Zaatari and the Obstacles They Face." Amal and Zeena decided that "Mom" should go with us and make the trip a family experience. Lina agreed to join us and shortly thereafter we left for Jordan.

Amal posted our travel plans on her Facebook page and words of encouragement and commitments for financial contributions started to show up on her FB page. This was for the purchase of much-needed supplies. A dear friend dropped in at our home on Christmas Eve to deliver a huge bag of wound-care supplies. She wished us well on our planned trip and also made a generous monetary donation through the SAMS office. The donations provide much-needed help for all the services that SAMS provides.

We arrived in Amman on December 27, 2015 and a spent few days visiting with family and friends before the rest of the group arrived. The seventy-plus group members were mostly from the USA with a few from Europe, Canada and UAE, and most arrived a little before New Year's Eve. Several medical and dental students from Jordan were among the volunteers who joined us.

*Omar, Zeena, and Amal at the Orientation Session
on January 1, 2016*

At 7:00 pm, on the first day of January, I went to an orientation meeting with Amal and Zeena. The weather was very cold with snow falling, making the streets of Amman wickedly slippery and dangerous to drive on. I was afraid of driving my old Honda on Amman's streets at night with the road conditions being as perilous as they were.

But Amal was "on a mission" and wouldn't have her plans sent on a detour. "Dad, snow or not, we need to be there," she said. So, I called my brother Ahmad and asked him if he would drive us to the camp in his four-wheel drive vehicle. He was most agreeable and we set off into the snowy, darkness.

My good friend, William (Bill) Burke, President of the Georgia chapter of the Association on the Prevention of Blindness, was already en route to Amman via Paris. Bill had decided earlier to join our volunteer team after we had lunch and talked about our respective holiday plans. Bill had been to Jordan many times over the prior two decades, beginning in 1994. I felt Bill had missed the friends and "family" he had made in Jordan over the past 20 years, and like our family, could accomplish multiple tasks in a single visit.

Before my departure, I called the SAMS office in Washington to ask if Bill could join us. I was told the mission was full, but they would make an exception for Bill. He flew out of Atlanta on New Year's Eve and arrived in Amman on the evening of January 1, 2016. He was too late for the introductory meeting, but made his way to our home.

At the orientation meeting, held at a local hotel, a young Syrian doctor named Bassel Atassi took the lead and gave an introductory presentation on Zaatari and what to expect, what to do, and what not to do. Dr. Atassi appeared to be in his early thirties, a graduate of the Jordan University of Science and Technology School of Medicine in Irbid, not too far from the Al-Zaatari Camp. After completion of medical school in Jordan, Bassel had done his hematology-oncology training in the USA and was currently practicing in Chicago.

Bassel was at ease in his role as mission leader and knew almost all of the seventy volunteers on the mission trip. Many of them had been there before. He greeted each person by first name and knew everyone's specialty. He even slipped in few funny remarks about the heart surgeon who was going to serve as a dental assistant! He had done his homework and knew a lot about each of us. We were all very impressed.

For me as a cardiac surgeon, it wasn't possible to do cardiac operations in the refugee camps or any of the small affiliated hospitals. Thus, my stated role was to help Amal with her work and I knew then that Amal's prophecy was about to be realized.

The next morning at 6:00 am, my alarm went off and I checked my email. The weather conditions were acceptable for the 120-kilometer trip to northern Jordan. The travel plans were a "go," as the snow was light during the night and road conditions were much improved. The temperature was hovering above freezing and we were advised to dress warmly, since the Zaatari clinics weren't heated.

We left our Amman home at 7:00 am and drove to the hotel where the rest of the group was assembling. Two buses and a mini-van were waiting to take the group to the designated clinics at Zaatari and some additional refugee camps in Jordan. Ms. Jinan Shbat, our trip coordinator, and the local SAMS team in Amman had everything organized. We were given sheets of paper with our listed names, which bus we were to ride on, and which clinical site to attend. Every day for the next six days, they provided details on our assignments, leaving no question of the duty posts or what the responsibilities for the day would be. They did an amazing job of organizing all aspects of the trip—a truly remarkable accomplishment!

The buses moved out and the mission had officially begun. During the hour-and-a-half bus ride to Zaatari, I was apprehensive about what to expect and emotionally uptight about meeting mothers, dads, and children in the camp.

A multitude of stories had been written about Zaatari; many aroused fear. Some may have been true while many were perhaps fiction. We were all apprehensive about the upcoming encounter, so I prepared myself for an emotionally taxing (and possibly depressing) situation. I wondered if I was the only one with this fear of the unknown. But after overhearing conversations and discussing my own apprehensions with Amal, Zeena, and Bill, I realized that we were all in the same boat. It seemed that many of the other were apprehensive, too

As we approached the camp, the first security checkpoint came into view. We had to show the armed guards our identification papers so our well-prepared team leaders presented the required documents. Even carrying more weight, we had the approval from the Jordanian Ministry of Health to provide medical care to the camp population. When we returned each morning and departed each evening, the same procedures were followed. We learned that the guards would only allow people with special permits to enter or exit the camp.

Zaatari, we learned, was home to eighty-six thousand inhabitants, mostly women and children. The male population was comprised of older men, with very few young or middle-aged men. Many of the women were widowed, typically mothers caring for their orphaned children. All were products of a brutal war that started as part of the infamous and ill-fated "Arab Spring."

The war in Syria had become a war made up of smaller battles between many different parties, religious sects, armies, terrorist groups, and others. They were supported (or allegedly supported) by regional or international powers who gave assistance either directly or in a clandestine manner.

For me, it was hard to tell who was fighting who and for what reasons. So I decided that I would focus only on providing medical care to anyone who needed it. I would ask no questions about the residents' ethnic or political affiliations.

That was the simplest way to deal with complex and changing alliances. Caring for the needy without being concerned about political affiliations was in keeping with my medical oath, my long-standing training, and how I practiced in the United States. In my career as a surgeon in Atlanta, I operated on and treated many victims of violence: stab wounds, gunshot wounds, and worse. I provided the same best care possible to hard-core criminals as I did to innocent victims. Once an ill or injured person became my patient, I had a responsibility to be his/her best health advocate and never asked questions about any irrelevant personal history. All patients deserved the best care, no questions asked. I decided to apply those principles at Zaatari. That plan made my work simpler, and it wouldn't ruffle any feathers or cause any mini-international incidents.

The "refugee camp" was surrounded by barbed wire in all directions, with a heavy police presence. We were told that in its heyday, the camp housed nearly 200,000 people, coming from differing towns and cities, often from conflicting backgrounds. Until security was tightened, the camp was a place of many conflicts, not dissimilar from those back in Syria.

The Jordanian government established the tight security for the benefit of all the camp residents and helped ensure that the aid donated by other countries made it to the people in the camps.

On the first day, I visited the dental clinic. It was a 10x30-foot mobile wood and steel structure fitted with three functional dental chairs and basic dental care necessities. Unfortunately, the X-ray machine was broken. The electricity in the camp was unreliable, but thanks to our gas-powered generator, the power supply to the clinic continued non-stop.

I quickly realized that my ability to contribute to the dental services was rather limited. My experience in dentistry consisted only being as a patient in my dentist's office! So, I offered my help to our dental team on an as-needed basis. It was graciously accepted, and only used occasionally. As it turned out later, my relations in the country proved most valuable to my daughter and her colleagues.

In a camp with 86,000 residents (and many of them children), you can only imagine how busy the clinic was. On the first two days, I volunteered in the emergency room, where I saw several children with second degree burns on their arms, legs, and chest, all resulting from scalding water falling on their small bodies. I came to know a provider named Mohammed; a man in his early forties, tall, handsome, with a neatly trimmed beard.

Mohammed was soft-spoken and it seemed that he was there all the time; examining and treating these small patients and showing a wonderful kind and amazing spirit. He showed genuine care as he consoled each child, cleaning the burn or injury site, apply a soothing cream impregnated with anti-bacterial topical agents, and instructing the parents on further care.

I saw several cases of severe tonsillitis. I remember two children, ages 7 and 9 years, from a family of three children. The dad told me that at night, the children coughed most of the time and complained of difficulty in breathing. In the USA, we would have admitted these children and closely monitored them for any signs of impending upper airway obstruction. This option wasn't available at Zaatari. We prescribed antibiotics with instructions for patient to return to the clinic if a fever didn't go way or if symptoms persisted. In several cases, we kept patients in the clinic and gave them initial doses of intravenous antibiotics; them we dispensed additional oral antibiotics.

Being a cardiothoracic surgeon, I was out of my complex specialty for these few days. There was no cardiac surgical operating room, no ICU, and no surgical team. Thus, I became the local "expert surgeon" to see potential surgical cases that needed further evaluation or referral.

On one occasion, I was asked by an internist to evaluate a young woman who had fainted in her clinic. My exam revealed she was tachycardic, with a heart rate of 112 beats per minute. She also had a low-grade fever of 37.6° C (about 99.68° F). and vague abdominal and flank pain. I suggested that we obtain a complete blood count to assess if she had evidence of infection, and urinalysis to see whether the source of her pain was a urinary tract infection (UTI). My recommendations were accepted. I left the follow-up to the internist, since I was convinced that the patient didn't have a "surgical abdomen." I hope the patient well.

I also saw a young man with a dry cough and fever. I ordered a chest X-ray and to my surprise, there was a right upper-lobe lesion. My colleagues and I reviewed the film and became concerned that he might have pulmonary tuberculosis (TB). Thus, we immediately separated him from the rest of the patients and notified the camp administrator to arrange for further testing outside the camp. We learned that in north Jordan there was a "Christian Hospital" that had been in existence for many years. It treated TB patients. We arranged for our patient to have an appointment there the following day.

On the following days, I spent part of my time helping my friend Bill Burke and my daughter Zeena with Bill Burke's visual screening exams. The clinic waiting room was barely-roofed, with the assembly area "equipped" with metal benches, lined up in parallel. With the ambient temperature approaching the freezing point, those metal benches were awfully cold. Every day, we would work in the unheated and painfully cold damp clinics. To stay warm, we wore several layers of heavy clothing. We avoided freezing until the heat from our bodies and that of our patients would warm the clinics' metal walls.

Bill Burke with Samir to his left and two other camp children

In the eye clinic, we examined children as young as two years of age and adults, as well—some in their late sixties and seventies. No one was turned away. Bill brought individually wrapped candies to give to each child after her or his exam. Those treats always brought a smile to their precious faces.

The eye clinic quickly became "the candy store" for the camp kids. It was difficult to stick to our plans: one exam, one candy, with no return unless asked by the provider. We were forced to ration the candy and use it only for the specific purpose intended—a reward for being a good patient.

One day, three young boys about ten years of age showed up on for their eye exams. Their eyesight was found to be good and each was given a piece of candy. They left, only to return with several new kids, each to be examined and given a piece of candy. We immediately realized that the three children (Samir, Abdullah, and Abdul Kader) had become our strongest recruiters. They would go out into the camp, explain to the adults about the free eye exam and bring other children in. The three boys became a *de facto* part of our team; recruiting patients and explaining where to stand and how to focus.

The next day, Samir, the most vocal and assertive of the three, showed up and asked, "Where is Ms. Zeena?" He wanted to help Zeena recruit more children who needed to get their eyes examined. The following day, he returned and asked for "Aunt Zeena" and again helped guide young boys and girls to the eye clinic for examinations. To our surprise, he never asked for another piece of candy or failed to follow the rules we had set for him. Samir was cooperative, always showing up upon our arrival and leaving the clinic at 11:00 am to attend his school. He would always return before our afternoon departure to say goodbye.

In the afternoon, Samir would hang around and ask questions about where we came from and how we had become doctors. I could tell that there was a lot of thinking going on in that child's mind. Seizing on the opportunity, I encouraged him to take his school seriously. He seemed to understand that in order to become a doctor, he had to intently focus on his education. He would nod his head in the affirmative.

Samir became a frequent visitor and a valuable assistant in our clinic. Before and after school, we would find him hanging around, often waiting to talk to Zeena.

He was quiet, inquisitive, and had piercing eyes. Samir was a good-looking kid; round-faced, light-skinned, with dirty, blond hair. He was skinny; barely weighing fifty-pounds. He was extremely polite, always wanting to help, but never getting in the way.

We all took a liking to Samir and would inquire about him when he wasn't around. We soon realized that each one of us looked forward to seeing him every day. Bill said, "I couldn't get this child out of my head." Interestingly, Zeena and I had the same feelings toward Samir!

The dental clinic was very busy on the first two days and all three dentists rarely had a break. Emma joined by Mohammed, another graduate of Boston University's School of Dental Sciences. Also, there was Tareq, another energetic dentist who had finished dental school in Syria and had received additional training in the United States, where he currently practiced. In their first two days, they collectively performed over one hundred complex extractions, cavity repairs, and other dental- surgical procedures on camp residents.

The dentists were the first to begin work each morning and the last to finish each evening. Their waiting room was full the entire day and they never left camp until the last patient had been seen. The last bus leaving camp each evening was for the dental team.

On the morning of the third day, devastating news came from the camp director. He instructed the dental team to cease and desist! They could no longer provide dental care to the camp patients with the stated reason that the clinic was not "certified!"

The bad news came down hard on all of us; particularly on Amal and her two colleagues. They went to Dr. Bassel and Jinan to ask what could be done. They were just as dumbfounded and speechless as Amal's team was! They searched through their permission documents, and to their surprise, found one that contained a sentence at the end of the approval letter, excluding dental clinics! And to make matters even worse, the document was received on New Year's Eve, when most of the volunteers were already in Jordan.

This struck the dental team like a lightning bolt. They were upset, frustrated and angry. Amal came to me and said, "Dad, we need your help in getting back to treating our patients. You have many influential friends in Jordan."

"But rules are rules," I said, "It will be hard, if not impossible, to reverse the decision. Let's go back to Amman."

That wasn't the answer Amal wanted to hear! She replied, "We came to Jordan on a mission and we are going to complete it. We are not taking 'no' for an answer."

She went on: "Give me your Jordanian cell phone. I'm going to call the people you know and ask them to help."

And that's exactly what she did. She first called a dear friend who had hosted a wonderful dinner for us and few more friends at one of Amman's nicest restaurants a few days earlier. My friend, a highly respected former Prime Minster of Jordan, took Amal's call. She explained to him what had happened and asked for his help to allow her and her colleagues to finish the task for which they had come from thousands of miles away to perform.

In the next few hours Amal was making calls to, and receiving calls from, important government officials, including the Minister of Health. While all of this was going on, Amal, had one of her dental students on the team post the "Dental Shutdown" story on Facebook. It also listed my Jordan cell number for "helpers" to call.

One phone call came from a young woman who asked to speak to Amal. The caller was the daughter of an official of the Zaatari camp. She offered to call her dad and ask him to help resolve the problem. Over the next few hours, Amal and her dental colleagues were politicking phone, trying their best to get back to work.

Later, Amal learned that the person who came and shut them down was the father of her new Facebook "friend" who had called earlier. Promptly, Amal pulled my phone, searched through the "recent calls" and called the young woman back. "So, it was your dad who shut us down? What is his phone number? Can I call him and ask him to allow us to go back to work?"

Amal called the officer, told him she was a "friend" of his daughter and pleaded for help. She told him that they incurred so much expense and hardship to come on this mission to help the needy refugees with whom they had bonded. The officer replied in the kindliest way, not uncommon for Jordanians, that he would do his best to intervene and get them back to work.

By late afternoon, we were becoming more optimistic that the goodness of the Jordanian officials would turn the tide in our favor. Why would any official stand in the way of the good the teams were making in the lives of these refugees?

The next day, we decided to take our chances and make the ninety- minute drive to the camp, in hopes that approval had been granted. As we assembled at 9:30 am, a gentleman arrived at the clinic and introduced himself as camp vice-director with permission to resume work in the dental clinics.

Within minutes, patients were in the dental chairs being anesthetized and undergoing much-needed procedures. It was another super busy day for the three young American dentists.

The dental clinic had twice as many patients as the other clinics: those who hadn't been treated the previous day, in addition to those already scheduled for that day. The dentists had a double load and worked non-stop all day long with no breaks and no lunches. The three of them treated one patient after the other until all were seen. No one was turned away. They upheld their responsibilities to their patients and to their profession.

My three-year-old child from a long time ago had convinced me that she had become a serious adult and determined professional in every way. My image of Amal changed forever in my mind. It took the Zaatari camp experience to show me that Amal was no longer a child!

On our flight home, Amal shared an encounter she had had with the crowds who were competing to be treated. It was very chaotic and disruptive until she stepped into the waiting area and stated her policy. "Please write your name on this sheet of paper. First come, first served. I will not leave until all of you are treated. Once you enter my clinic, you will be my private patient. In my clinic, you will not be refugees, you will be my patients. You will be treated with the same respect and attention I treat my patients in the United States." From then on, the clinics ran smoothly.

As we were winding down our work on this mission, we compiled the numbers on what we had completed in the clinics that week. Over 350 children and adults had their eyes examined with about forty major vision problems found. Amal and her colleagues had treated three-hundred plus dental patients. As we sat in the bus waiting for our return to Amman for the last time, I noticed a little child sitting on the side of the road with his back to the corner of a small trailer and a nearby water tank. His head was bowed down and he was almost motionless. I watched him for few minutes and he didn't move from this position. He seemed to me to be depressed or terribly sad.

I looked closer and realized that the boy was my friend Samir. I assumed that he knew we were departing and would not be back again. In his own way, he wanted to say farewell, but didn't want to impose on us. I turned to Bill and said, "Bill, can I have a handful of candy? I want to give it to Samir and say goodbye."

Bill quickly reached into his bag, grabbed a handful of candy. He said, "Please do. I can't get Samir out of my head!"

I grabbed the candy and started to step out of the bus to hand Samir the candy when Zeena said, "Dad, please let me have the candy. I want to give to Samir."

She then stepped out of the bus, walked toward Samir, knelt on the ground before him and extended her hand, full of candy. From my seat, I could plainly see Samir's hand reaching out for the candy with his head still pointing to his feet.

The bus filled up and the driver indicated that it was time to leave. I called out to Zeena, but she signaled me to wait! A few minutes later, Zeena came back to the bus and took her seat without saying a word. Her eyes did all the talking with tears flowing down her face.

As the bus moved out, Zeena was sobbing. Bill and I were speechless. Samir remained in his bowed-head position as our view of him quickly faded. We could remove Samir from our field of vision, but not from our heads or our hearts. He has stayed with us as a living memory of the Al-Zaatari camp and all the people suffering from the painful war in Syria.

Back in Amman that evening, I met with the Dean of the Jordanian Medical School and two of my cardiac surgical colleagues. We discussed possibilities of collaboration to provide future cardiac surgery care to the refugees. The dean and his faculty were very supportive.

As we departed Amman and returned to our home in Atlanta, Samir became the symbol of the Al-Zaatari camp. He will stay in our memory for years to come. We all went to Zaatari to treat patients and heal refugees, which we did. In return, Zaatari healed my inner soul and made me a more caring physician. Many of my colleagues felt the same way. Zaatari was a life-changing experience that will stay with me for the rest of my life. And as this mission came to an end, I said goodbye to my little friend, Samir.

Time to Dance with Children at Al Zaatari

Goodbye Samir. I hope we will meet again!

CHAPTER TWENTY

We Became Brothers

Farewell, William F. Burke

W e were born of different parents, and thousands of miles apart. We grew up in different cities, different cultures, played different games, and spoke different languages when we were children. Yet, when we met nearly twenty-five years ago, we connected.

Our backgrounds were totally different. He was white and I am brown; he was Christian, and I'm Muslim; he went to school in Alabama, while I went to school in Jordan, Tennessee, and Georgia.

As children, he grew up in the South; I grew up in the tumultuous Middle East. And as we both grew older, we each went to different colleges. I studied medicine and he studied business. We had nothing in common.

But when we met for the first time over coffee in 1992, we hit it off right away. I am not sure why, but we did.

Soon after our first meeting, I invited him and his wife Jana to join Lina and me to see a play at the Fox Theater. The play was "Jesus Christ Superstar."

Years later, Bill told me with a smile on his face, "I thought you were pulling my leg. What is this Muslim guy doing inviting me to a play about Jesus Christ?"

Bill ran my cardiac surgery practice in Atlanta and helped me organize my practice in Jordan, when I relocated to Amman from 1994 to 2000.

And so, it was ironic that we became the best of friends. We organized and held conferences on telemedicine and international health around the world. We were young and full of energy, and had great hopes and we aspired to make the world a better and healthier place.

Bill travelled to my hometown, Amman, no less than fifteen times over the span of 20 years.

He became a well-known figure in the old city of Amman. Bill was dear to all my brothers and sisters, nieces and nephews. In truth, he'd become a member of our family.

Year after year, Bill would make visits to Jordan where he visited Petra, the Dead Sea, and Jerash. He became familiar with downtown Amman, its back streets, the local restaurants, and the sweet shops. His favorite shop was Habibah Kunafah. That was a must-have every time Bill visited Amman.

In January 2016, Bill went with my daughters and me to provide much-needed medical care at Zaatari, a Syrian refugee camp in north Jordan. He was touched by the stories of hardships experienced by the refugees and he, like the rest of us, came back a different human being.

Again, in January 2017, Bill joined my daughters and me on another trip to serve the increasing number of Syrian refugees in Jordan.

Bill became so enamored with the country and the people of Jordan, that he made plans to relocate to Amman and take a job in administration. He loved the country of Jordan and its people, and those who knew him reciprocated that love.

Sadly, Bill's life came to unexpected, tragic end, depriving his friends and family of the love and affection that Bill always shared with all who were blessed to have known him.

All the Lattouf brothers miss Bill, for he was one of us. All our nephews and nieces will also miss him. They considered him an uncle and always looked forward to seeing him. He was very special to each of them.

All my friends adored Bill. He became their dear friend. They loved him.

He became one of us.

Bill, you will be missed. May you Rest in Peace.

Omar M Lattouf
Atlanta April 5, 2017

William F. Burke

Made in the USA
Columbia, SC
13 May 2017